CALIFORNIA

PRENTICE HALL

S0-AJW-757

WORLD HISTORY
THE MODERN WORLD

Reading and Note Taking Study Guide

Copyright © by Pearson Education, Inc., publishing as Pearson Prentice Hall, Boston, Massachusetts 02116.
All rights reserved. Printed in the United States of America. This publication is protected by copyright, and permission should be obtained from the publisher prior to any prohibited reproduction, storage in a retrieval system, or transmission in any form or by any means, electronic, mechanical, photocopying, recording, or likewise. For information regarding permission(s), write to: Rights and Permissions Department, One Lake Street, Upper Saddle River, New Jersey 07458.

Pearson Prentice Hall™ is a trademark of Pearson Education, Inc.
Pearson® is a registered trademark of Pearson plc.
Prentice Hall® is a registered trademark of Pearson Education, Inc.

PEARSON
Prentice Hall

Boston, Massachusetts
Upper Saddle River, New Jersey

ISBN 0-13-133349-6

19 20 21 22 23 24 25   V011   17 16 15 14 13

Contents

© Pearson Education, Inc., publishing as Pearson Prentice Hall. All rights reserved.

© Pearson Education, Inc., publishing as Pearson Prentice Hall. All rights reserved.

© Pearson Education, Inc., publishing as Pearson Prentice Hall. All rights reserved.

© Pearson Education, Inc., publishing as Pearson Prentice Hall. All rights reserved.

How to Use This Book

The **Reading and Note Taking Study Guide** will help you better understand the content of *Prentice Hall World History.* This book will also develop your reading, vocabulary, and note taking skills.

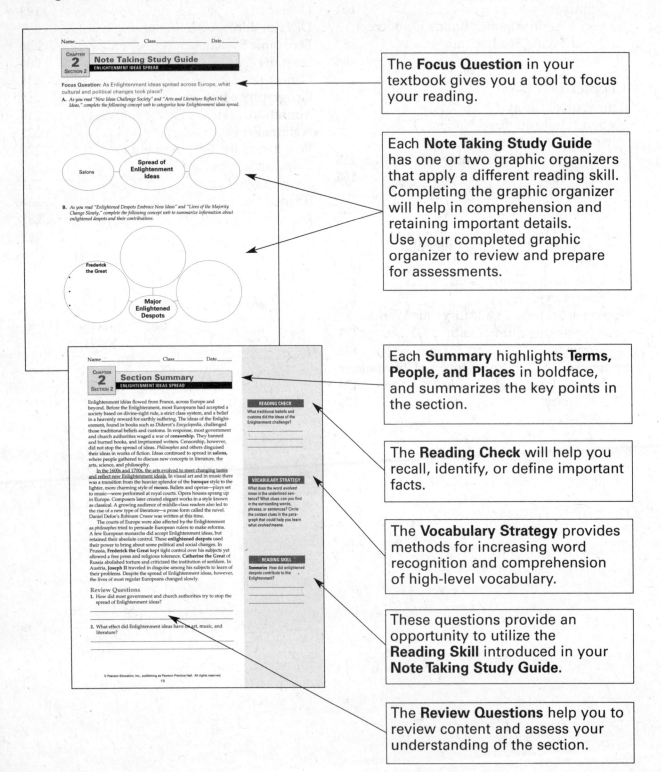

The **Focus Question** in your textbook gives you a tool to focus your reading.

Each **Note Taking Study Guide** has one or two graphic organizers that apply a different reading skill. Completing the graphic organizer will help in comprehension and retaining important details. Use your completed graphic organizer to review and prepare for assessments.

Each **Summary** highlights **Terms, People, and Places** in boldface, and summarizes the key points in the section.

The **Reading Check** will help you recall, identify, or define important facts.

The **Vocabulary Strategy** provides methods for increasing word recognition and comprehension of high-level vocabulary.

These questions provide an opportunity to utilize the **Reading Skill** introduced in your **Note Taking Study Guide.**

The **Review Questions** help you to review content and assess your understanding of the section.

© Pearson Education, Inc., publishing as Pearson Prentice Hall. All rights reserved.

Concept Connector Worksheets support the **Concept Connector** features and the **Concept Connector Cumulative Review** found in each chapter of your text, as well as the **Concept Connector Handbook** found at the end of your textbook. These worksheets will help you to compare key concepts and events and to see patterns and make connections across time. The thematic essay portion of each worksheet will prepare you for social studies exams and assessments.

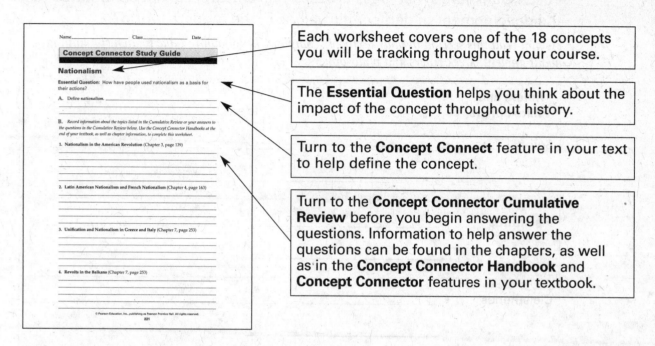

Each worksheet covers one of the 18 concepts you will be tracking throughout your course.

The **Essential Question** helps you think about the impact of the concept throughout history.

Turn to the **Concept Connect** feature in your text to help define the concept.

Turn to the **Concept Connector Cumulative Review** before you begin answering the questions. Information to help answer the questions can be found in the chapters, as well as in the **Concept Connector Handbook** and **Concept Connector** features in your textbook.

Thematic essays are an important part of social studies exams and assessment tests. This portion of the Concept Connector Worksheet provides sample topics for thematic essays.

Prepare an outline for the sample topic. Use the information from the chapters and **Concept Connector Handbook** to develop your outline.

Model Outline

© Pearson Education, Inc., publishing as Pearson Prentice Hall. All rights reserved.

Note Taking Study Guide

CHAPTER 1 SECTION 1

THE GREEK ROOTS OF DEMOCRACY

Focus Question: What ideas arose in ancient Greece that contributed to the development of democratic values in the modern world?

As you read this section in your textbook, complete the following table to identify main ideas about ancient Greek rulers and philosophers.

Rulers and Philosophers	Ideas	
Solon	• _____ • _____	• _____
Pisistratus	• _____ • _____	• _____
Cleisthenes	• _____ • _____	• _____
Pericles	• _____ • _____	• _____ • _____
Socrates	• _____ • _____	• _____ • _____
Plato	• Believes Reason led to knowledge • Should regulate citizens lives • Ideas, working of every rulers	• Rejected Athenian Democracy • Equality of people at birth • Unfrican society as Hierarch1/00 allowed
Aristotle	• Government of many • city-state the best • Praded Reason • _____	• Constitutional govern. • Hated tyranny • _____

© Pearson Education, Inc., publishing as Pearson Prentice Hall. All rights reserved.

Name_____ Class_____ Date_____

The ancient Greeks built small, independent **city-states.** Each was a political unit made up of a city and the surrounding lands. The two most influential city-states were **Sparta** and **Athens.** While Sparta stressed stern discipline, Athens glorified the individual and extended political rights to more citizens.

In many Greek city-states, the government started as a **monarchy** and evolved into an aristocracy. The Spartan government included two kings and a council of elders who advised the monarchs. It was in Athens that the idea of **democracy** first took root. Under an aristocracy, Athenian wealth and power had grown. Discontent, however, spread among ordinary people; merchants and soldiers resented the power of the nobles. This discontent led to the rise of **tyrants,** who often won the support of the merchant class and the poor by making reforms that helped these groups. The Athenian tyrant Cleisthenes broadened the role of ordinary citizens in government and set up a genuine **legislature.** In this way, tyrants moved Athens toward democracy.

After winning the Persian Wars, Athens emerged as the most powerful city-state in Greece. Under the able statesman **Pericles,** the government became more democratic. Pericles believed that all male citizens, regardless of wealth or social class, should take part in government. In addition to serving in the Athenian assembly, male citizens over 30 years of age served on a **jury** for a year. In a civic speech, Pericles praised the Athenian form of government, stating that power was in the hands "not of a minority but of the whole people."

Greek philosophers also contributed greatly to the development of Western political thought. The philosopher **Socrates** was a longtime defender of democracy. He maintained that the duties of the individual included submitting to the laws of the state. His student **Plato** rejected democracy and, instead, argued that the state should regulate every aspect of its citizens' lives to provide for their best interests. Plato's most famous student, **Aristotle,** favored a constitutional government and the rule of law. Aristotle argued that even rulers must be subject to the law. This principle lies at the heart of all modern constitutional governments.

Review Questions

1. How did tyrants win the support of the people?

The tyrants won the support of _people through reforms._

2. How did Pericles directly involve male citizens in Athens' government?

Pericles involved male citizens over _30 served in juries for a year._

READING CHECK

In which Greek city-state did the idea of democracy first take root?

The first greek _city-state that had_ _the idea of Democracy_ _was Athens_

VOCABULARY STRATEGY

What does the word *civic* mean in the underlined sentence? Note that the word *civic* comes from the Latin word for "citizen." Use your prior knowledge of the word *citizen* and context clues to help you figure out what *civic* means.

READING SKILL

Identify Main Ideas What were Plato's main ideas about government?

Plato's main idea _of government_ _rejected democracy_

© Pearson Education, Inc., publishing as Pearson Prentice Hall. All rights reserved.

Name_____ Class_____ Date_____

Focus Question: How did the government of Rome develop into an empire?

A. *As you read "Establishing a Republic" in your textbook, complete the following chart to understand the effects of changes in Rome's government.*

From Monarchy to Republic

Effects

- Senate becomes powerful body vs. Monarchy
  Common people demanded equality
- Senators made the law
- Plebians gained the right to elect their own tribunes
- Plebians gains access to power and safeguards for their rights.

B. *As you read "From Republic to Empire" in your textbook, complete the following chart to identify causes and effects of Rome's development from a republic to an empire.*

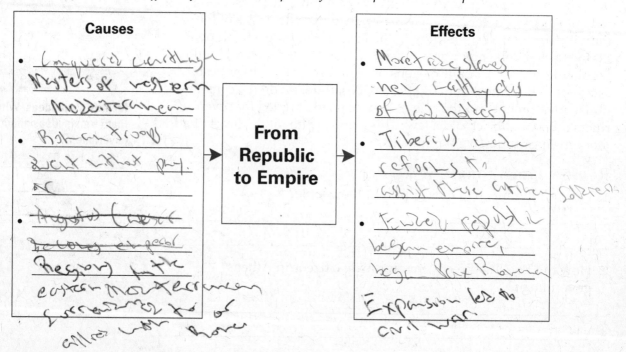

Causes

- Conquered coastlinge Masters of western Mediterranean
- Roman troops went without pay. no
- Augustus Civest factory emperor Region with eastern Mediterranean Expansion to allies with Rome

From Republic to Empire

Effects

- More trade, slaves, new wealthy class of land holders
- Tiberius made reforms to assist those without soldiers
- Ended republic began empire, began Pax Romana
- Expansion led to civil war

© Pearson Education, Inc., publishing as Pearson Prentice Hall. All rights reserved.

CHAPTER 1 SECTION 2 — Section Summary

THE ROMAN REPUBLIC AND EMPIRE

In 509 B.C., after driving out the Etruscans, the Romans set up a new government called a **republic.** The Romans thought a republic would keep any individual from gaining too much power. The 300 members of the republic's senate were all patricians—the landholding upper class. Senators, who served for life, made the laws.

Each year, the senators elected two **consuls** from among the patricians. The consuls supervised the business of government and commanded Rome's armies. In the event of war, the senate might choose a **dictator** to temporarily take complete control over the government. The common people, or plebeians, made up the bulk of the Roman population. In time, the plebeians influenced government to have the laws written down in the Twelve Tables. They also gained the right to elect their own officials, called **tribunes.** The tribunes could **veto** laws passed by the senate that were harmful to plebeians.

As Rome's political system evolved, its armies expanded Roman power into the eastern Mediterranean. On the north coast of Africa, the Romans also destroyed the city-state of **Carthage** and established themselves as masters of the western Mediterranean. Expansion, however, created problems. At issue was who should hold power— the senate or popular political leaders looking to enact reforms. Soon Rome was plunged into civil war.

One military commander, **Julius Caesar,** emerged from the chaos and seized control. Although Caesar kept the senate and other features of the republic, he forced the senate to make him dictator. Jealous and fearful of his power, Caesar's enemies stabbed him to death. Caesar's grand-nephew Octavian became the new ruler. The senate gave Octavian the title **Augustus Caesar,** and he became the first emperor.

During the time known as the *Pax Romana,* the Roman empire brought peace, order, unity, and prosperity to the lands it ruled. Trade flowed freely to and from distant lands in Africa and Asia. Merchants carried ivory, gold, spices, silk, and other commodities. People spread ideas as they traveled. The greatest legacy of Rome, however, was the establishment of justice through the law. In the 400s, the emperor **Justinian,** in what was now the eastern Byzantine empire, reformed the Roman law code. Later, this code influenced the Christian church and medieval monarchs.

Review Questions

1. Why did the Romans set up a republic?

They set up a republic to limit any individual from gaining too much power

2. How did Roman expansion in the Mediterranean affect Rome?

Roman expansion lead to civil war because people didn't know who should hold power

READING CHECK

Which Roman ruler forced the senate to name him dictator?

The Roman Ruler who forced the senate to have him dictator was Julius Caeser

VOCABULARY STRATEGY

What does *commodities* mean in the underlined sentence? What clues to its meaning can you find in the nearby words? Circle the words in the sentence that could help you learn what *commodities* means.

READING SKILL

Understand Effects Identify two effects of Roman rule under the empire.

The Roman rule brought Peace, order, unity and prosperity.

© Pearson Education, Inc., publishing as Pearson Prentice Hall. All rights reserved.

Note Taking Study Guide
PRINCIPLES OF JUDAISM

Focus Question: Why did the concept of law mean so much to the Jewish people?

As you read this section in your textbook, complete the chart below by listing positive and negative events in Jewish history that were effects of obedience or disobedience to God's laws.

Negative Events	Positive Events
• Enslaved by Egypt for 400 Years	• Escaped from Egypt, Temple by moses, build a temple dedicated to God.
	• Made a covenant with God for protection
• The scattering of the Jews, Babylon captured in 586 B.C.	• Recieved 10 commandments
• Because it spread, they lost contact by power/trade. Romans destroyed temple in 66 A.D.	• Culture remained central to Judea after hysteria resistance.

© Pearson Education, Inc., publishing as Pearson Prentice Hall. All rights reserved.

Section Summary

PRINCIPLES OF JUDAISM

Most of what we know about the ancient Israelites, or the Jews, comes from the Torah, their most sacred text. The story begins with **Abraham,** who, in Canaan, founded what became the Israelite nation. Later, a famine forced many Israelites to migrate to Egypt, where they spent more than 400 years as enslaved workers. An Israelite named **Moses** finally led his people in their exodus from Egypt.

To the Israelites, each event in their history reflected God's plan for them. They were **monotheistic,** believing in one God. Their belief in this one God dominated their lives. In this way their beliefs differed from those of nearby peoples. Other ancient peoples invoked particular gods as special protectors, believing that such gods were tied to certain places.

The Israelites believed that God had made a **covenant** with Abraham and his descendants. God promised not only to protect the Israelites but also to provide them with a homeland. To fulfill their part of the covenant, the Israelites believed that they had to remain faithful and obedient to God's laws. The Torah set out many laws, including the Ten Commandments. The first four Commandments stress religious duties of the individual toward God, such as keeping the **Sabbath,** a holy day for rest and worship. The other Commandments set out rules for individual conduct toward others.

Often in Israel's history, spiritual leaders emerged to interpret God's will. These **prophets** warned that failure to obey God's law would lead their people to disaster. Other prophets preached a strong code of **ethics.** The Israelites saw their leaders as fully human and bound to obey God's law. In this way, the culture and religion of Judaism contributed to the rise of another important democratic concept, the rule of law.

The Babylonian Captivity in 586 B.C. marked the start of the **diaspora,** or scattering of the Jews. When that captivity ended, not all Jews returned to Canaan, later called Palestine. The scattering of the Jews went on for centuries. In 63 B.C., Rome conquered **Jerusalem,** the capital of the independent Jewish state of Judea in Palestine. Now the Roman general Pompey turned Judea into a Roman province.

Review Questions

1. How did the religious beliefs of the Israelites differ from those of other ancient peoples?

Other ancient peoples believed particular gods as special protectors, believing that such gods were tied to certain places.

2. How is the Torah related to the Israelites' covenant with God?

It set laws for the Israelites to follow. Ten commandments.

READING CHECK

To what democratic concept did Judaism contribute?

The jewish culture contributes the rule of law.

VOCABULARY STRATEGY

What does the word *invoked* mean in the underlined sentence? The word comes from the Latin word *vocare,* which means "to call." Use the meaning of the Latin root and context clues to help you figure out what *invoked* means.

READING SKILL

Understand Effects What did the Israelites believe would happen if they failed to obey God's law?

They will not receive protection from God

© Pearson Education, Inc., publishing as Pearson Prentice Hall. All rights reserved.

CHAPTER 1 SECTION 4

Note Taking Study Guide
THE RISE OF CHRISTIANITY

Focus Question: How did Christianity develop from Judaism into a powerful, independent religion?

As you read this section in your textbook, complete the flowchart below by identifying causes and effects related to the rise of Christianity.

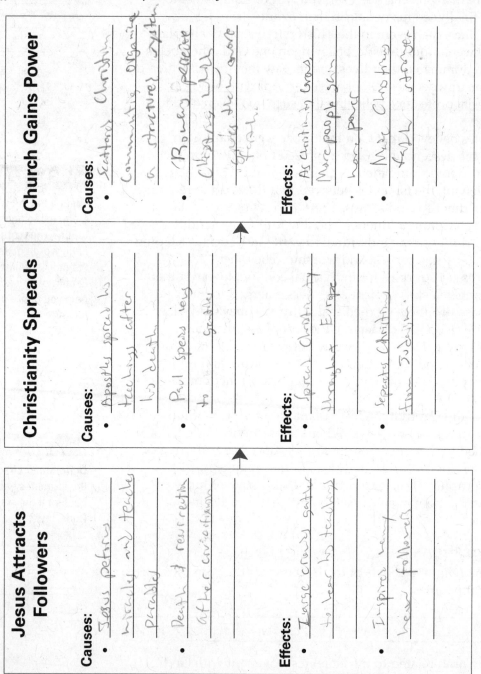

Church Gains Power

Causes:
- Scattered Christian Communities organized a structured system
- Bishops regulate Christian beliefs
- Church grew more powerful

Effects:
- As Christianity grows, more people join
- More power
- Made Christianity faith stronger

Christianity Spreads

Causes:
- Apostles spread his teachings after his death
- Paul spreads very to the Gentiles

Effects:
- Spread Christianity throughout Europe
- Separates Christianity from Judaism

Jesus Attracts Followers

Causes:
- Jesus preform miracles and teaches Parables
- Death & resurrection after his crucifixion

Effects:
- Large crowds gather to hear his teachings
- Inspires many new followers

© Pearson Education, Inc., publishing as Pearson Prentice Hall. All rights reserved.

Section Summary

THE RISE OF CHRISTIANITY

Early in the *Pax Romana*, Christianity emerged in the Roman provinces of Galilee and Judea. Its leader was a Jewish man named **Jesus.** Almost all that we know about his life comes from the New Testament Gospels. Among other things, they relate that Jesus preached in Jerusalem. Twelve close followers, or **apostles,** helped him. Large crowds gathered to hear Jesus, especially when word spread that he had performed miracles.

Jesus' teachings were rooted in Jewish law, but he interpreted the law in new ways. He promised to bring salvation and eternal life to anyone who would believe in him. He emphasized God's love and taught the need for justice, morality, and service to others. But Jewish leaders were concerned that Jesus' teaching might trigger a revolt and a Roman crackdown. They had Jesus arrested. Roman authorities crucified him. The Gospels state that Jesus rose from the dead. After these events, the apostles and other followers spread Jesus' teachings. **Paul,** a Jew from Asia Minor, brought Jesus' teachings to Gentiles, or non-Jews. He helped to make Christianity separate from Judaism and to develop into a world religion.

However, for a time Christianity remained a sect within Judaism. The main difference between this sect and traditional Judaism was the Christian focus on Jesus as the **messiah** and the center of their faith. Rome had a long history of **tolerance** of varied religions, but that tolerance did not extend to Christianity. Christians refused to make sacrifices to the emperor and would not honor Roman gods. Although the Romans persecuted Christians, Christianity continued to spread.

Gradually, the scattered Christian communities organized a structured church hierarchy made up of **clergy,** such as priests and bishops. During the Middle Ages, the Christian church became the most powerful force in Europe.

In the West, the shared heritage of Jews and Christians is known as the Judeo-Christian tradition. At the heart of this tradition are the moral and ethical principles put forth in the Bible. These principles are the basic assumptions behind many Western beliefs, including fair treatment, or justice.

Review Questions

1. What did Jesus promise to those who believed in him?

Jesus' promise that he would bring salvation and
eternal life.

2. What was the main difference between the new Christian sect and traditional Judaism?

Christians believe that Jesus is the messiah
while Jewish people don't.

READING CHECK

Who was Paul?

A Jew from Asia Minor that
spread Jesus' teaching to Gentiles
_____

VOCABULARY STRATEGY

What does the word *hierarchy* mean in the underlined sentence? The word *hierarchy* is a synonym for the words *order* and *rank*. Use these synonyms and any context clues to help you figure out what *hierarchy* means.

READING SKILL

Identify Causes and Effects
Why did the Roman empire not tolerate Christianity, and what was the result?

Because Christians refused
to sacrifice and honor
Roman gods, persecuted them

© Pearson Education, Inc., publishing as Pearson Prentice Hall. All rights reserved.

Note Taking Study Guide

DEMOCRATIC DEVELOPMENTS IN ENGLAND

Focus Question: How did Parliament emerge victorious in the struggle for political power in medieval England?

As you read this section in your textbook, complete the chart below with the multiple causes of the developments in democracy that took place in England.

Growth of Royal Power	Evolving Traditions of Government	Triumph of Parliament
Causes:	Causes:	Causes:
• New system of rule called feudalism makes the monarch a powerful lord.	• Magna Carta makes rule of law a key principle of government	• People went revolt against Charles I
• Strong monarchy — William the Conqueror gained firm control over their lands	• Great Council evolves into Parliament	• Cromwell's army defeats the King's troops in the English civil war.
• Courts collect system to effective tax increase royal authority	• Parliament wins the right to approve new taxes which limits the powers of the monarch	• House of Commons abolishes the monarchy
• Establishment of common law Royal justice system		• Restoration; Glorious Revolution; English Bill of Rights

© Pearson Education, Inc., publishing as Pearson Prentice Hall. All rights reserved.

Section Summary
DEMOCRATIC DEVELOPMENTS IN ENGLAND

During the early Middle Ages, European monarchs needed protection from invasion. In response to this need for security, a new system of rule known as **feudalism** evolved. In this system, lesser lords pledged their service and loyalty to greater lords, with the greatest lord—the king—at the top of the feudal pyramid.

Royal power continued to grow. When **William the Conqueror** became king of England, he had a census taken and used this information to build an efficient system of tax collecting. Later, during the reign of King **Henry II**, judges traveled throughout England to enforce royal laws. The decisions of these royal courts became the foundation of English **common law.** Unlike local feudal laws, common law applied to the whole of England. It standardized laws and punishments.

English kings repeatedly clashed with nobles and the church, as each tried to dominate in England. Out of those power struggles evolved new traditions of government. For example, the document called the Magna Carta contained two very important principles— that citizens had certain rights and that even the monarch must obey the law. As Parliament developed, it won the right to approve any new taxes. In this way Parliament could check, or limit, the power of the monarch.

In 1625 when Charles I became king, he ruled as an **absolute monarch.** He tried to dissolve Parliament and run the government without it. The struggle between Charles I and Parliament became so great that civil war erupted. Parliament's forces, led by **Oliver Cromwell,** defeated the king's troops. After a trial, Charles I was executed—a clear signal that no English ruler in the future could ignore the rule of law.

After some later turmoil, Parliament offered the crown to William and Mary of Orange. Before they could be crowned, they had to accept the English Bill of Rights, which restated the traditional rights of English citizens, such as trial by jury. It also abolished cruel or unjust punishments and affirmed the principle of **habeas corpus.** The English Bill of Rights established a type of government called a **limited monarchy.** English rulers had to obey the law and work with Parliament. These events in England's history were important to the development of democracy.

Review Questions

1. How did common law differ from feudal laws?

_____

_____

2. What principles did the English Bill of Rights establish?

_____

_____

READING CHECK

What document did William and Mary have to accept before they could become monarchs of England?

_____

_____

_____

VOCABULARY STRATEGY

What does the word *dominate* mean in the underlined sentence? The word comes from the Latin word *dominus,* which means "master." Use the meaning of the Latin root and context clues to help you learn what *dominate* means.

READING SKILL

Recognize Multiple Causes
Identify the causes of civil war between Parliament and Charles I.

_____

_____

_____

© Pearson Education, Inc., publishing as Pearson Prentice Hall. All rights reserved.

CHAPTER **2** SECTION 1	**Note Taking Study Guide**
	PHILOSOPHY IN THE AGE OF REASON

Focus Question: What effects did Enlightenment philosophers have on government and society?

As you read this section in your textbook, complete the following table to summarize each thinker's works and ideas.

Thinkers' Works and Ideas	
Hobbes	• *Leviathan* • Believes in absolute monarchy the social contract
Locke	• Two Treatises of Government, • Believed in natural rights, • Believed in Limited government
Montesquieu	• • •
	• • •
	• • • •
	• •
	• • •

© Pearson Education, Inc., publishing as Pearson Prentice Hall. All rights reserved.

CHAPTER 2 SECTION 1

Section Summary

PHILOSOPHY IN THE AGE OF REASON

In the 1500s and 1600s, the Scientific Revolution introduced reason and scientific method as the basis of knowledge, changing the way people looked at the world. In the 1700s, scientific successes, such as a vaccine against smallpox, convinced educated Europeans of the power of human reason. **Natural law**—rules discovered by reason— could be used to study human behavior and solve society's problems. In this way, the Scientific Revolution sparked another revolution in thinking, known as the Enlightenment.

The ideas of **Thomas Hobbes** and **John Locke,** two seventeenth-century English thinkers, were key to the Enlightenment. Hobbes argued that people are "brutish" by nature, and therefore need to be controlled by an absolute monarchy. According to Hobbes, people enter into a **social contract** with their government, giving up their freedom in exchange for an organized society. In contrast, Locke thought that people are basically reasonable and moral. He also believed that people have certain **natural rights,** including the right to life, liberty, and property. Locke rejected absolute monarchy, believing that the best kind of government had limited power. In fact, Locke felt that people could overthrow a government if it violated their natural rights.

In France, Enlightenment thinkers called *philosophes* believed that the use of reason could lead to reforms in government, law, and society. Baron de **Montesquieu** proposed the ideas of separation of powers and of checks and balances as a way to protect liberty. His ideas would deeply affect the Framers of the United States Constitution. With his biting wit, **Voltaire** exposed abuses of power and defended the principle of freedom of speech. Denis **Diderot** edited a 28-volume *Encyclopedia*. <u>This work included articles on human knowledge, explaining new ideas on topics such as government, philosophy, and religion.</u> **Jean-Jacques Rousseau** believed that the good of the community should be placed above individual interests. However, the Enlightenment slogan "free and equal" did not apply to women.

Other thinkers, including **Adam Smith,** focused on using natural laws for economic reform. They rejected government regulation of the economy and instead urged the policy of **laissez faire.**

Review Questions

1. How did the Scientific Revolution lead to the Enlightenment?

_____

_____

2. Identify three major ideas developed by Enlightenment thinkers.

_____

_____

READING CHECK

Who were the *philosophes* and what did they believe?

_____

_____

_____

VOCABULARY STRATEGY

What does the word *philosophy* mean in the underlined sentence? It comes from a Greek word that means "love of wisdom." Use this word-orgins clue to help you figure out what *philosophy* means.

READING SKILL

Summarize What ideas did Thomas Hobbes and John Locke have about human nature and the role of government?

_____

_____

© Pearson Education, Inc., publishing as Pearson Prentice Hall. All rights reserved.

CHAPTER 2 SECTION 2
Note Taking Study Guide
ENLIGHTENMENT IDEAS SPREAD

Focus Question: As Enlightenment ideas spread across Europe, what cultural and political changes took place?

A. *As you read "New Ideas Challenge Society" and "Arts and Literature Reflect New Ideas," complete the following concept web to categorize how Enlightenment ideas spread.*

B. *As you read "Enlightened Despots Embrace New Ideas" and "Lives of the Majority Change Slowly," complete the following concept web to summarize information about enlightened despots and their contributions.*

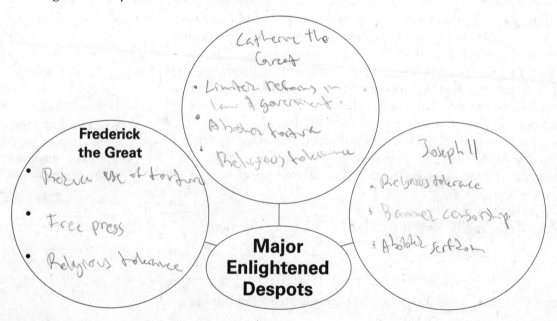

© Pearson Education, Inc., publishing as Pearson Prentice Hall. All rights reserved.

CHAPTER 2 — SECTION 2

Section Summary
ENLIGHTENMENT IDEAS SPREAD

Enlightenment ideas flowed from France, across Europe and beyond. Before the Enlightenment, most Europeans had accepted a society based on divine-right rule, a strict class system, and a belief in a heavenly reward for earthly suffering. The ideas of the Enlightenment, found in books such as Diderot's *Encyclopedia*, challenged those traditional beliefs and customs. In response, most government and church authorities waged a war of **censorship.** They banned and burned books, and imprisoned writers. Censorship, however, did not stop the spread of ideas. *Philosophes* and others disguised their ideas in works of fiction. Ideas continued to spread in **salons,** where people gathered to discuss new concepts in literature, the arts, science, and philosophy.

In the 1600s and 1700s, the arts evolved to meet changing tastes and reflect new Enlightenment ideals. In visual art and in music there was a transition from the heavier splendor of the **baroque** style to the lighter, more charming style of **rococo.** Ballets and operas—plays set to music—were performed at royal courts. Opera houses sprang up in Europe. Composers later created elegant works in a style known as classical. A growing audience of middle-class readers also led to the rise of a new type of literature—a prose form called the novel. Daniel Defoe's *Robinson Crusoe* was written at this time.

The courts of Europe were also affected by the Enlightenment as *philosophes* tried to persuade European rulers to make reforms. A few European monarchs did accept Enlightenment ideas, but retained their absolute control. These **enlightened despots** used their power to bring about some political and social changes. In Prussia, **Frederick the Great** kept tight control over his subjects yet allowed a free press and religious tolerance. **Catherine the Great** of Russia abolished torture and criticized the institution of serfdom. In Austria, **Joseph II** traveled in disguise among his subjects to learn of their problems. Despite the spread of Enlightenment ideas, however, the lives of most regular Europeans changed slowly.

Review Questions

1. How did most government and church authorities try to stop the spread of Enlightenment ideas?

   They tried to stop the spread of ideas by imposing censorship, burning books, and imprisonment

2. What effect did Enlightenment ideas have on art, music, and literature?

   It affected art, music, and literature by transitioning it into the style of baroque and rococo

© Pearson Education, Inc., publishing as Pearson Prentice Hall. All rights reserved.

READING CHECK

What traditional beliefs and customs did the ideas of the Enlightenment challenge?

It challenges divine-right rule, strict class system, and a belief in a heavenly reward for earthly suffering.

VOCABULARY STRATEGY

What does the word *evolved* mean in the underlined sentence? What clues can you find in the surrounding words, phrases, or sentences? Circle the context clues in the paragraph that could help you learn what *evolved* means.

READING SKILL

Summarize How did enlightened despots contribute to the Enlightenment?

They contributed to the Enlightenment by making reforms.

CHAPTER 2 SECTION 3

Note Taking Study Guide

BIRTH OF THE AMERICAN REPUBLIC

Focus Question: How did ideas of the Enlightenment lead to the independence and founding of the United States of America?

As you read this section in your textbook, complete the following timeline with the dates of important events that led to the formation of the United States.

French and Indian War ends.

1763

1760

© Pearson Education, Inc., publishing as Pearson Prentice Hall. All rights reserved.

In the mid-1700s, Britain was a formidable global power. Key reasons for this status included its location, support of commerce, and huge gains in territory around the world. <u>Furthermore, the new king, **George III**, began to assert his leadership and royal power.</u>

Britain's growing empire included 13 prosperous colonies on the east coast of North America. The colonists shared many values. These included an increasing sense of their own destiny separate from Britain. In some cases, Britain neglected to enforce laws dealing with colonial trade and manufacturing.

Tensions between the colonists and Britain grew as Parliament passed laws, such as the **Stamp Act,** that increased colonists' taxes. The colonists protested what they saw as "taxation without representation." A series of violent clashes with British soldiers intensified the colonists' anger. Finally, representatives from each colony, including **George Washington** of Virginia, met in the Continental Congress to decide what to do. Then in April 1775, colonists fought British soldiers at Lexington and Concord, and the American Revolution began.

On July 4, 1776, the Second Continental Congress adopted the Declaration of Independence. Written primarily by **Thomas Jefferson,** it reflects John Locke's ideas about the rights to "life, liberty, and property." It also details the colonists' grievances and emphasizes the Enlightenment idea of **popular sovereignty.**

At first, chances for American success looked bleak. The colonists struggled against Britain's trained soldiers, huge fleet, and greater resources. When the colonists won the Battle of Saratoga, other European nations, such as France, joined the American side. With the help of the French fleet, Washington forced the British to surrender at **Yorktown, Virginia,** in 1781. Two years later American, British, and French diplomats signed the **Treaty of Paris**, ending the war.

By 1789, leaders of the new United States, such as **James Madison** and **Benjamin Franklin,** had established a **federal republic** under the Constitution. The new government was based on the separation of powers, an idea borrowed directly from Montesquieu. The Bill of Rights, the first ten amendments to the Constitution, protected basic rights. The United States Constitution put Enlightenment ideas into practice and has become an important symbol of freedom.

Review Questions

1. What first caused tensions to rise between the colonists and Britain?

_____

_____

2. What are some Enlightenment ideas found in the Declaration of Independence?

_____

_____

READING CHECK

How did France help the Americans win the Revolution?

_____

_____

_____

VOCABULARY STRATEGY

What does the word *assert* mean in the underlined sentence? What context clues can you find in the surrounding words, phrases, or sentences that hint at its meaning? Circle the word below that is a synonym for *assert*.

1. declare

2. deny

READING SKILL

Recognize Sequence Place the events leading to the American Revolution in the correct order.

_____

_____

_____

© Pearson Education, Inc., publishing as Pearson Prentice Hall. All rights reserved.

Note Taking Study Guide

ON THE EVE OF REVOLUTION

Focus Question: What led to the storming of the Bastille, and therefore, to the start of the French Revolution?

As you read this section in your textbook, complete the following chart by identifying the multiple causes of the French Revolution.

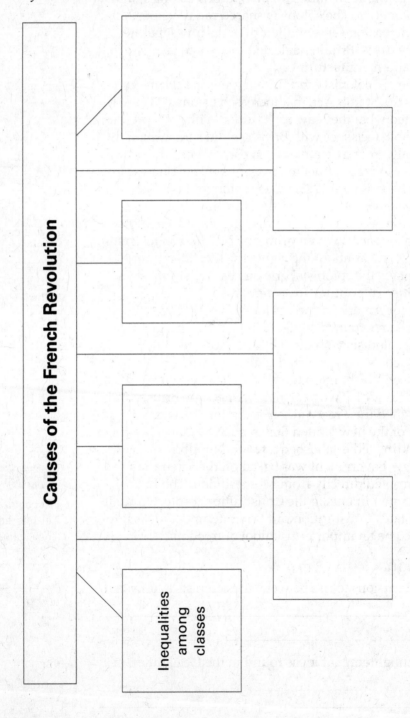

Causes of the French Revolution

Inequalities among classes

© Pearson Education, Inc., publishing as Pearson Prentice Hall. All rights reserved.

CHAPTER 3 SECTION 1

Section Summary
ON THE EVE OF REVOLUTION

Under France's **ancien régime**, there were three social classes, or **estates**. The First Estate was the clergy, who enjoyed great wealth and privilege. The Second Estate was the titled nobility. They held top jobs in government, the army, and the courts. The vast majority of the population, including the **bourgeoisie**, or middle class, formed the Third Estate. The bulk of the Third Estate consisted of rural peasants. The poorest members of the Third Estate were urban workers.

Members of the Third Estate resented the privileges enjoyed by their social "betters." The First and Second Estates, for example, were exempt from most taxes, while peasants paid taxes on many things, including necessities. Then Enlightenment ideas led people to question the inequalities of the old social structure. The Third Estate demanded that the privileged classes pay their share.

Economic troubles added to the social unrest. **Deficit spending** had left France deeply in debt. In the 1780s, bad harvests sent food prices soaring. **Louis XVI** chose **Jacques Necker** as an economic advisor. Later, the king was forced to dismiss Necker for proposing to tax the First and Second Estates. The crisis deepened. Powerful nobles and clergy called for a meeting of the **Estates-General** to try to control reform. Louis XVI finally set a meeting at Versailles. Beforehand, the king asked all three estates to prepare **cahiers** listing their grievances. Some lists demonstrated the high level of resentment among the classes.

The Estates-General met in May 1789. After weeks of stalemate, delegates of the Third Estate abandoned the Estates-General and formed the National Assembly. Later, when they were locked out of their meeting place, the members of the new legislature took their famous **Tennis Court Oath.** They swore never to separate until they had established a just constitution.

On July 14, 1789, the streets of Paris buzzed with rumors that royal troops were going to occupy the city. More than 800 Parisians assembled outside the **Bastille,** demanding weaponry stored there. When the commander refused, the enraged mob stormed the Bastille, sparking the French Revolution.

Review Questions

1. How was society structured under France's *ancien régime?*

_____

_____

2. What economic troubles did France face in the 1780s?

_____

_____

READING CHECK

Which group paid the most taxes?

_____

_____

_____

VOCABULARY STRATEGY

What does the word *urban* mean in the underlined sentence? Notice that the word *rural* appears in the previous sentence. *Rural* is an antonym of *urban.* Use the meaning of the antonym to help you figure out what *urban* means.

READING SKILL

Recognize Multiple Causes Identify three causes of the French Revolution.

_____

_____

_____

© Pearson Education, Inc., publishing as Pearson Prentice Hall. All rights reserved.

CHAPTER 3 SECTION 2

Note Taking Study Guide

THE FRENCH REVOLUTION UNFOLDS

Focus Question: What political and social reforms did the National Assembly institute in the first stage of the French Revolution?

As you read this section in your textbook, complete the following outline by identifying the main ideas and supporting details in this section.

I. **Political crisis leads to revolt**

  A. The Great Fear

    1. Inflamed by famine and rumors

    2. Demonstrated peasant anger with an unjust regime.

  B. Paris commune comes to power

    1. Revolutionary activist factions compete for power

    2. Paris Commune replace royalist govern in city.

II. The National assembly acts

  A. Special Provleges

    1. Feudalism is abolished.

    2. Equality of all were citizens before the law

  B. Declaration of the rights of men

    1. Declarations of the Rights of men were were all equal before the law

    2. Did not include women

  C. Women march on Versailles

    1. Versaille women march to Versailles to see King

    2. Angry at Marie Antoinette

III. _____

  A. _____

    1. _____

    2. _____

  B. _____

    1. _____

    2. _____

  C. _____

    1. _____

    2. _____

(Outline continues on the next page.)

© Pearson Education, Inc., publishing as Pearson Prentice Hall. All rights reserved.

Note Taking Study Guide
THE FRENCH REVOLUTION UNFOLDS

(Continued from page 24)

IV. _____
   A. _____
      1. _____
      2. _____
   B. _____
      1. _____
      2. _____
   C. _____
      1. _____
      2. _____
   D. _____
      1. _____
      2. _____

© Pearson Education, Inc., publishing as Pearson Prentice Hall. All rights reserved.

CHAPTER 3 SECTION 2

Section Summary
THE FRENCH REVOLUTION UNFOLDS

READING CHECK

Who were the sans-culottes?

Working class
men/women.

In France, the political crisis of 1789 coincided with a terrible famine. Peasants were starving and unemployed. In such desperate times, rumors ran wild. Inflamed by famine and fear, peasants unleashed their fury on the nobles. Meanwhile, a variety of **factions** in Paris competed to gain power. Moderates looked to the **Marquis de Lafayette** for leadership. However, a more radical group, the Paris Commune, replaced the city's royalist government.

The storming of the Bastille and the peasant uprisings pushed the National Assembly into action. In late August, the Assembly issued the Declaration of the Rights of Man and the Citizen. <u>It proclaimed that all male citizens were equal before the law.</u> Upset that women did not have equal rights, journalist **Olympe de Gouges** wrote a declaration that provided for this. The Assembly did not adopt it, however. Nor was King Louis XVI willing to accept reforms. Much anger was directed at the queen, **Marie Antoinette,** who lived a life of great extravagance.

VOCABULARY STRATEGY

What do you think the word *proclaimed* means in the underlined sentence? The words *proclamation, declaration,* and *announcement* are all synonyms for *proclaimed.* Use what you know about these synonyms to figure out the meaning of *proclaimed.*

The National Assembly produced the Constitution of 1791. This document reflected Enlightenment goals, set up a limited monarchy, ensured equality before the law for all male citizens, and ended Church interference in government.

Events in France stirred debate all over Europe. Some applauded the reforms of the National Assembly. Rulers of other nations, however, denounced the French Revolution. Horror stories were told by **émigrés** who had fled France. Rulers of neighboring monarchies increased border patrols to stop the spread of the "French plague" of revolution.

In October 1791, the newly elected Legislative Assembly took office, but falling currency values, rising prices, and food shortages renewed turmoil. Working-class men and women, called **sans-culottes,** pushed the revolution in a more radical direction, and demanded a **republic.** The sans-culottes found support among other radicals, especially the **Jacobins.** The radicals soon held the upper hand in the Legislative Assembly. Eager to spread the revolution, they declared war against Austria and other European monarchies.

READING SKILL

Identify Supporting Details Identify two aspects of the Constitution of 1791 that reflect Enlightenment goals.

Limited monarchy
Ended church
interference of
government.

Review Questions

1. What was the Declaration of the Rights of Man and the Citizen? Why were some people dissatisfied with it?

   It proclaimed that all male citizens were both equal
   before the law. People were upset because it didn't include
   women

2. How did rulers of European monarchies react to the French Revolution?

   They responded by denouncing the revolution.

© Pearson Education, Inc., publishing as Pearson Prentice Hall. All rights reserved.

Focus Question: What events occurred during the radical phase of the French Revolution?

As you read this section in your textbook, complete the following timeline to show the sequence of events that took place during the radical phase of the French Revolution.

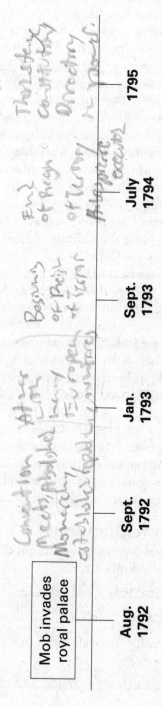

Timeline events:

- **Aug. 1792** — Mob invades royal palace
- **Sept. 1792** — Convention at its first meeting abolishes Monarchy, establishes republic
- **Jan. 1793** — King Louis executed (tried for treason)
- **Sept. 1793** — Beginning of Reign of Terror
- **July 1794** — End of Reign of Terror, Robespierre executed
- **1795** — Third constitution, Directory in Paris

© Pearson Education, Inc., publishing as Pearson Prentice Hall. All rights reserved.

CHAPTER 3
SECTION 3

Section Summary
RADICAL DAYS OF THE REVOLUTION

READING CHECK

Who was Robespierre?

_____

_____

_____

VOCABULARY STRATEGY

What do you think *radical* means in the underlined sentence? Notice that the word *more* appears before *radical*. Use the word *more* and your prior knowledge to help you figure out what *radical* means.

READING SKILL

Recognize Sequence What occurred after the radicals took control of the Assembly in 1792?

_____

_____

_____

In 1793, the revolution entered a frightening and bloody phase. The war with Austria was not going well for France. Some felt the king was in league with France's enemies. Others wanted to restore the king's power. On August 10, 1792, a mob stormed the royal palace. Radicals then took control of the Assembly and called for the election of a new legislative body called the National Convention. **Suffrage** was to be extended to all male citizens, not just to those who owned property. The Convention that met in September 1792 was a more radical body than earlier assemblies. It voted to abolish the monarchy and establish the French Republic. Louis XVI and his queen were executed.

War with other European nations and internal rebellions concerned the government. The Convention created the Committee of Public Safety to deal with these issues. It had almost absolute power. Jacobin Maximilien **Robespierre** led the Committee. He was one of the chief architects of the **Reign of Terror,** which lasted from September 1793 to July 1794. During that time, courts conducted hasty trials for those suspected of resisting the revolution. Many people were the victims of false accusations. About 17,000 were executed by **guillotine.**

In reaction to the Terror, the revolution entered a third stage, dominated by the bourgeoisie. It moved away from the excesses of the Convention, and moderates created the Constitution of 1795. This set up a five-man Directory to rule, and a two-house legislature. However, discontent grew because of corrupt leaders. Also, war continued with Austria and Britain. Politicians planned to use **Napoleon** Bonaparte, a popular military hero, to advance their goals.

By 1799, the French Revolution had dramatically changed France. It had dislodged the old social order, overthrown the monarchy, and brought the Church under state control. **Nationalism** spread throughout France. From the city of **Marseilles,** troops marched to a rousing new song that would become the French national anthem. Revolutionaries also made social reforms. They set up systems to help the poor and abolished slavery in France's Caribbean colonies.

Review Questions

1. What type of government did the National Convention establish in September 1792?

Committee of Public Safety, radical body

_____

2. Identify three changes that the French Revolution brought to France.

_____

_____

© Pearson Education, Inc., publishing as Pearson Prentice Hall. All rights reserved.

Name_____ Class_____ Date_____

Focus Question: Explain Napoleon's rise to power in Europe, his subsequent defeat, and how the outcome still affects Europe today.

As you read this section in your textbook, complete the flowchart to list the main ideas about Napoleon's rise to power and his defeat.

Napoleon quickly advances through military ranks.

CHAPTER 3 SECTION 4

Section Summary
THE AGE OF NAPOLEON

READING CHECK

What was the Napoleonic Code?

_____

_____

_____

The final phase of the revolution is known as the Age of Napoleon. When the revolution first broke out, Napoleon Bonaparte was a young lieutenant. Battle victories fueled his ambitions and his rise through army ranks. By 1804, Napoleon had acquired enough power to assume the title Emperor of the French. At each step on his rise to power, Napoleon had held a **plebiscite.** However, he still had absolute power, although he was elected.

Napoleon consolidated his power by strengthening the central government. His economic and social reforms won support across classes. Among his most lasting reforms was the **Napoleonic Code.** This new code of laws embodied Enlightenment principles of equality, religious tolerance, and the abolition of feudalism.

From 1804 to 1812, Napoleon battled the European powers and created a vast French empire. A brilliant general, before each battle Napoleon developed a new plan. <u>In this way, opposing generals could never anticipate what he would do next.</u> He rarely lost. Napoleon **annexed** the Netherlands, Belgium, and parts of Italy and Germany to build his Grand Empire. However, Britain remained outside Napoleon's grasp. His attempt to wage economic warfare against Britain through the **Continental System** failed. Many Europeans resented the scarcity of goods. Growing nationalism led to resistance against French influence. In Spain, patriots waged **guerrilla warfare** against the French.

In 1812, Napoleon invaded Russia with 600,000 soldiers. To avoid battles with Napoleon, the Russians retreated, burning crops and villages as they went. This **scorched-earth policy** left the French hungry and cold. Most of the Grand Army was destroyed. Fewer than 20,000 soldiers survived. The retreat from Moscow through the long Russian winter shattered Napoleon's reputation for success.

In 1815, British and Prussian forces crushed the French at the Battle of Waterloo. Napoleon was forced to **abdicate.** After Waterloo, diplomats met at the **Congress of Vienna** to restore stability and order in Europe after years of revolution and war. The Congress strived to create a lasting peace through the principle of **legitimacy** and by maintaining a balance of power. Leaders also met periodically in the **Concert of Europe** to discuss problems that threatened peace.

VOCABULARY STRATEGY

What do you think the word *anticipate* means in the underlined sentence? What clues can you find in the surrounding words and phrases? Use these context clues to figure out the meaning of *anticipate.*

READING SKILL

Identify Main Ideas Write a new title for this section Summary to express the main idea in another way.

_____

_____

_____

Review Questions

1. How did the French respond to Napoleon's economic and social reforms?

_____

_____

2. Why did Napoleon's invasion of Russia fail?

_____

_____

© Pearson Education, Inc., publishing as Pearson Prentice Hall. All rights reserved.

Note Taking Study Guide

AN AGE OF IDEOLOGIES

Focus Question: What events proved that Metternich was correct in his fears?

A. As you read "Conservatives Prefer the Old Order," and "Liberals and Nationalists Seek Change," fill in the table to identify main ideas about conservatism, liberalism, and nationalism.

Conservatism	Liberalism	Nationalism
• _____	• _____	• _____
• _____	• _____	_____
• _____	• _____	_____
• _____	• _____	
• _____	• _____	
• _____	• _____	
• _____		

B. As you read "Central Europe Challenges the Old Order," use the table to identify supporting details about revolts in Serbia, Greece, and other countries.

Serbia	Greece	Other Revolts
• _____	• _____	• _____
_____	_____	_____
• _____	• _____	• _____
_____	_____	_____
• _____	• _____	• _____
_____	_____	_____
• _____	• _____	
_____	_____	

© Pearson Education, Inc., publishing as Pearson Prentice Hall. All rights reserved.

Section Summary
AN AGE OF IDEOLOGIES

READING CHECK

What is universal manhood suffrage?

_____

_____

_____

VOCABULARY STRATEGY

What does the word *agitators* mean in the underlined sentence? Review the surrounding words and phrases to look for clues to its meaning. Use these context clues to help you understand what an *agitator* is.

READING SKILL

Identify Main Ideas What two groups generally struggled for political control during the early nineteenth century?

_____

_____

_____

After the Congress of Vienna, people with opposing **ideologies** plunged Europe into decades of turmoil. Conservatives, including monarchs, nobles, and church leaders, favored a return to the social order that had existed before 1789. They decided to work together in an agreement called the Concert of Europe. They wanted to restore the royal families that Napoleon had deposed. They supported a social hierarchy in which lower classes respected and obeyed their social superiors. They also backed established churches and opposed constitutional governments. Conservative leaders such as Prince Metternich of Austria sought to suppress revolutionary ideas.

Inspired by the Enlightenment and the French Revolution, liberals and nationalists challenged conservatives. Liberals included business owners, bankers, lawyers, politicians, and writers. They wanted governments based on written constitutions. They opposed established churches and divine-right monarchies. They believed that liberty, equality, and property were natural rights. They saw government's role as limited to protecting basic rights, such as freedom of thought, speech, and religion. Only later in the century did liberals come to support **universal manhood suffrage,** giving all men the right to vote. Liberals also strongly supported laissez-faire economics.

Nationalism gave people with a common heritage a sense of identity and the goal of creating their own homeland. In the 1800s, national groups within the Austrian and Ottoman empires set out to create their own states. Rebellions erupted in the Balkans, where there were people of various religions and ethnic groups. The Serbs were the first to revolt. By 1830, Russian support helped the Serbs win **autonomy,** or self-rule, within the Ottoman empire. In 1821, the Greeks revolted, and by 1830, Greece was independent from the Ottomans. Revolts spread to Spain, Portugal, and Italy. Metternich urged conservative rulers to crush the uprisings. In response, French and Austrian troops smashed rebellions in Spain and Italy.

In the next decades, sparks of rebellion would flare anew. Added to liberal and nationalist demands were the goals of the new industrial working class. By the mid-1800s, social reformers and agitators were urging workers to support socialism or other ways of reorganizing property ownership.

Review Questions

1. How did government views of conservatives and liberals differ?

_____

_____

2. Why did French and Austrian troops stop revolts in Spain and Italy?

_____

_____

© Pearson Education, Inc., publishing as Pearson Prentice Hall. All rights reserved.

Note Taking Study Guide
REVOLUTIONS OF 1830 AND 1848

Focus Question: What were the causes and effects of the revolutions in Europe in 1830 and 1848?

As you read this section, fill in the table below with a country, date, and main idea for each revolution of 1830 and 1848.

Revolutions of 1830 and 1848									
France	1830	Radicals force king to abdicate.							

© Pearson Education, Inc., publishing as Pearson Prentice Hall. All rights reserved.

Section Summary

REVOLUTIONS OF 1830 AND 1848

READING CHECK

What brought the Second Republic to an end?

_____

_____

_____

VOCABULARY STRATEGY

What does the word *denounced* mean in the underlined sentence? Reread the sentences before and after the underlined sentence. Were the French people happy or unhappy with Louis Philippe's government? Note that the government "tried to silence critics." Use these context clues to help you understand the meaning of *denounce*.

READING SKILL

Identify Main Ideas What is the main idea of the last paragraph in the Summary?

_____

_____

_____

When Louis XVIII died in 1824, Charles X inherited the French throne. In 1830, Charles suspended the legislature, limited the right to vote, and restricted the press. Angry citizens, led by liberals and **radicals,** rebelled and soon controlled Paris. Charles X abdicated. Radicals hoped to set up a republic, but liberals insisted on a constitutional monarchy. **Louis Philippe** was chosen king. As the "citizen king," Louis favored the bourgeoisie, or middle class, over the workers.

The Paris revolts inspired uprisings elsewhere in Europe. Most failed, but the revolutions frightened rulers and encouraged reforms. One notable success was in Belgium, which achieved its independence from Holland in 1831. Nationalists also revolted in Poland in 1830, but they failed to win widespread support. Russian forces crushed the rebels.

In the 1840s, discontent began to grow again in France. Radicals, socialists, and liberals denounced Louis Philippe's government. Discontent was heightened by a **recession.** People lost their jobs, and poor harvests caused bread prices to rise. When the government tried to silence critics, angry crowds took to the streets in February 1848. The turmoil spread, and Louis Philippe abdicated. A group of liberals, radicals, and socialists proclaimed the Second Republic. By June, the upper and middle classes had won control of the government. Workers again took to the streets of Paris. At least 1,500 people were killed before the government crushed the rebellion. By the end of 1848, the National Assembly issued a constitution for the Second Republic, giving the right to vote to all adult men. When the election for president was held, Louis Napoleon, the nephew of Napoleon Bonaparte, won. However, by 1852 he had proclaimed himself Emperor **Napoleon III.** This ended the Second Republic.

The revolts in Paris in 1848 again led to revolutions across Europe, especially in the Austrian empire. Revolts broke out in Vienna, and Metternich resigned. In Budapest, Hungarian nationalists led by **Louis Kossuth** demanded an independent government. In Prague, the Czechs made similar demands. The Italian states also revolted, and the German states demanded national unity. While the rebellions had some short-term success, most of them had failed by 1850.

Review Questions

1. What caused the rebellion in France in 1830?

_____

_____

2. In what parts of Europe did revolts take place following the Paris revolts of 1848?

_____

_____

© Pearson Education, Inc., publishing as Pearson Prentice Hall. All rights reserved.

Note Taking Study Guide

CHAPTER 4 SECTION 3

REVOLTS IN LATIN AMERICA

Focus Question: Who were the key revolutionaries to lead the movements for independence in Latin America, and what were their accomplishments?

As you read this section, fill in the table below with a country, a date, and a main idea for each of the revolts in Latin America.

Revolts in Latin America											
	Toussaint L'Ouverture leads an army of former slaves and ends slavery there.										
	1791										
	Haiti										

© Pearson Education, Inc., publishing as Pearson Prentice Hall. All rights reserved.

CHAPTER 4 SECTION 3

Section Summary
REVOLTS IN LATIN AMERICA

READING CHECK

What two leaders helped free much of South America?

_____

_____

_____

VOCABULARY STRATEGY

What does the word *proclaimed* mean in the underlined sentence? *Proclaim* comes from the Latin word *proclamare*. The prefix *pro-* means "before," and *clamare* means "to cry out" or "shout." Use these word-origin clues to help you to figure out the meaning of *proclaimed*.

READING SKILL

Identify Main Ideas In the first paragraph of the Summary, most of the sentences are supporting details. Which sentence states the main idea of that paragraph?

_____

_____

_____

By the late 1700s, revolutionary fever had spread to Latin America, where the social system had led to discontent. Spanish-born *peninsulares*, the highest social class, dominated the government and the Church. Many **creoles**—Latin Americans of European descent who owned the haciendas, ranches, and mines—resented their second-class status. **Mestizos**, people of Native American and European descent, and **mulattoes**, people of African and European descent, were angry at being denied the status, wealth, and power that the other groups enjoyed. The Enlightenment and the French and American revolutions inspired creoles, but they were reluctant to act. However, when Napoleon invaded Spain in 1808, Latin American leaders decided to demand independence from Spain.

Revolution had already erupted in Hispaniola in 1791 when **Toussaint L'Ouverture** led a slave rebellion there. The fighting cost many lives, but the rebels achieved their goal of abolishing slavery and taking control of the island. Napoleon's army tried to reconquer the island but failed. In 1804, the island declared itself independent under the name Haiti.

In 1810, a creole priest, **Father Miguel Hidalgo,** called Mexicans to fight for independence. After some successes, he was captured and executed. **Father José Morelos** tried to carry the revolution forward, but he too was captured and killed. Success finally came in 1821 when revolutionaries led by Agustín de Iturbide overthrew the Spanish viceroy and declared independence. Central American colonies soon declared independence, too.

In the early 1800s, discontent spread across South America. **Simón Bolívar** led an uprising in Venezuela. Conservative forces toppled his new republic, but Bolívar did not give up. In a grueling campaign, he marched his army across the Andes, swooping down into Bogotá and taking the city from the surprised Spanish. Then he moved south to free Ecuador, Peru, and Bolivia. There, he joined forces with another great leader, **José de San Martín.** San Martín helped Argentina and Chile win freedom from Spain. The wars of independence ended in 1824, but power struggles among South American leaders led to destructive civil wars. In Brazil, **Dom Pedro,** the son of the Portuguese king, became emperor and proclaimed independence for Brazil in 1822.

Review Questions

1. Why were creoles ready to revolt by 1808?

_____

_____

2. How did Brazil gain its independence?

_____

_____

© Pearson Education, Inc., publishing as Pearson Prentice Hall. All rights reserved.

CHAPTER
5
SECTION 1

Note Taking Study Guide
DAWN OF THE INDUSTRIAL AGE

Focus Question: What events helped bring about the Industrial Revolution?

As you read this section in your textbook, complete the following flowchart to list multiple causes of the Industrial Revolution.

© Pearson Education, Inc., publishing as Pearson Prentice Hall. All rights reserved.

CHAPTER
5
SECTION 1

Section Summary

DAWN OF THE INDUSTRIAL AGE

READING CHECK

Who formed the growing labor force for the Industrial Revolution?

_____

_____

_____

VOCABULARY STRATEGY

What does the word *statistics* mean in the underlined sentence? What prior knowledge do you have of this word? For example, think of where you may have seen statistics before. Use your prior knowledge and context clues in the sentence to help you learn what *statistics* means.

READING SKILL

Recognize Multiple Causes Identify three events in the agricultural revolution that caused population and industry to grow.

_____

_____

_____

The Industrial Revolution started in Britain. In 1750, most people worked the land, using handmade tools. They made their own clothing and grew their own food. With the onset of the Industrial Revolution, the rural way of life in Britain began to disappear. By the 1850s, many country villages had grown into industrial towns and cities. New inventions and scientific "firsts" appeared each year. Between 1830 and 1855, for example, an American dentist first used an **anesthetic** during surgery and a French physicist measured the speed of light.

A series of related causes helped spark the Industrial Revolution. It was made possible, in part, by another revolution—in agriculture—that greatly improved the quality and quantity of food. Farmers mixed different kinds of soils and tried out new methods of crop rotation to get higher yields. Meanwhile, rich landowners pushed ahead with **enclosure,** the process of taking over and consolidating land formerly shared by peasant farmers. As millions of acres were enclosed, farm output and profits rose. The agricultural revolution created a surplus of food, so fewer people died from starvation. Statistics show that the agricultural revolution contributed to a rapid growth in population.

Agricultural progress, however, had a human cost. Many farm laborers were thrown out of work. In time, jobless farm workers migrated to towns and cities. There, they formed a growing labor force that would soon operate the machines of the Industrial Revolution.

Another factor that helped trigger the Industrial Revolution was the development of new technology, aided by new sources of energy and new materials. One vital power source was coal, used to develop the steam engine. In 1764, Scottish engineer **James Watt** improved the steam engine to make it more efficient. Watt's engine became a key power source of the Industrial Revolution. Coal was also used in the production of iron, a material needed for the construction of machines and steam engines. In 1709, Adam Darby used coal to **smelt** iron, or separate iron from its ore. Darby's experiments led to the production of less-expensive and better-quality iron.

Review Questions

1. How did people's lifestyles change in Britain with the start of the Industrial Revolution?

_____

_____

2. Why was the steam engine important to the Industrial Revolution?

_____

_____

© Pearson Education, Inc., publishing as Pearson Prentice Hall. All rights reserved.

Note Taking Study Guide

BRITAIN LEADS THE WAY

Focus Question: What key factors allowed Britain to lead the way in the Industrial Revolution?

As you read this section in your textbook, complete the following concept webs to identify causes and effects of Britain's early lead in industrialization. Fill in the first concept web with causes. Fill in the second concept web with effects.

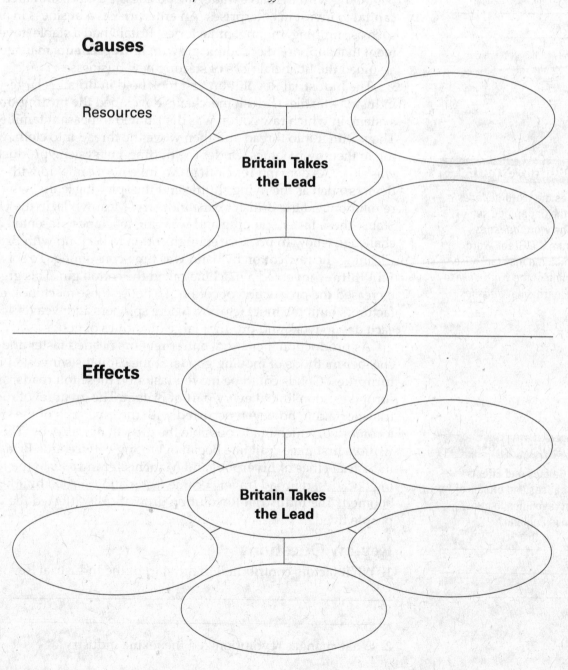

Causes

Resources

Britain Takes the Lead

Effects

Britain Takes the Lead

© Pearson Education, Inc., publishing as Pearson Prentice Hall. All rights reserved.

CHAPTER 5 SECTION 2

Section Summary
BRITAIN LEADS THE WAY

READING CHECK

What machine did Eli Whitney invent?

_____

_____

_____

VOCABULARY STRATEGY

What does the word *decades* mean in the underlined sentence? The word *decades* comes from the Greek word *deka,* which means "ten." Use the meaning of the word *deka* to help you learn what *decades* means.

READING SKILL

Identify Causes and Effects Identify causes and effects of the great revolution in transportation in England.

_____

_____

_____

The start of the Industrial Revolution in Britain can be attributed to many factors, including population growth and plentiful natural resources. The growing population and ready workforce boosted demand for goods. To increase production to meet the demand, however, another key ingredient was needed—money to start businesses. Beginning with the slave trade, the business class accumulated **capital** to invest in enterprises. An **enterprise** is a business in areas such as shipping, mining, or factories. Britain had a stable government that supported economic growth. **Entrepreneurs** managed and assumed the financial risks of starting new businesses.

The Industrial Revolution first took hold in Britain's largest industry—textiles. British merchants developed the **putting-out system,** in which raw cotton was distributed to peasant families. They spun it into thread and then wove the thread into cloth, working in their own homes. Under the putting-out system, production was slow. As demand for cloth grew, inventors came up with new devices, such as the flying shuttle and the spinning jenny, which revolutionized the British textile industry. Meanwhile, in the United States, these faster spinning and weaving machines presented a challenge—how to produce enough cotton to keep up with Britain. Cleaning the raw cotton by hand was time-consuming. To solve this, **Eli Whitney** invented a machine called the cotton gin. This greatly increased the production of cotton. To house these machines, manufacturers built the first factories, where spinners and weavers came each day to work and produce large quantities of goods.

As production increased, entrepreneurs needed faster and cheaper methods of moving goods. Some capitalists invested in **turnpikes.** Goods could be moved faster on these toll roads, and turnpikes soon linked every part of Britain. The great revolution in transportation, however, occurred with the invention of the steam locomotive, which made possible the growth of railroads. The world's first major rail line began operating between the British industrial cities of **Liverpool** and **Manchester** in 1830. <u>In the following decades, railroad travel became faster and railroad building boomed.</u> The Industrial Revolution dramatically affected the way people lived.

Review Questions

1. What factors contributed to the start of the Industrial Revolution?

_____

_____

2. What changes revolutionized the textile industry?

_____

_____

© Pearson Education, Inc., publishing as Pearson Prentice Hall. All rights reserved.

Note Taking Study Guide
SOCIAL IMPACT OF THE INDUSTRIAL REVOLUTION

Focus Question: What were the social effects of the Industrial Revolution?

As you read this section in your textbook, complete the following table to understand the effects of industrialization.

Industrialization

Challenges

- Crowded cities
-
-
-
-

Benefits

- Created jobs
-
-
-
-

© Pearson Education, Inc., publishing as Pearson Prentice Hall. All rights reserved.

CHAPTER 5 SECTION 3

Section Summary

SOCIAL IMPACT OF THE INDUSTRIAL REVOLUTION

READING CHECK

Who made up the new middle class that emerged during the Industrial Revolution?

Entrepreneur)

The Industrial Revolution brought rapid **urbanization,** or the movement of people to cities. Changes in farming, soaring population growth, and a demand for workers led masses of people to migrate from farms to cities. Almost overnight, small towns that were located around coal or iron mines grew into cities. Other cities developed around the factories in once-quiet market towns.

Those who benefited most from the Industrial Revolution were the entrepreneurs who set it in motion. The Industrial Revolution created this new middle class, whose members came from a variety of backgrounds. While the wealthy and the middle class lived in pleasant neighborhoods, vast numbers of poor struggled to survive in slums. They packed into tiny rooms in **tenements** that had no running water and no sewage or sanitation system. Sewage rotted in the streets or was dumped into rivers, which created an overwhelming stench and contaminated drinking water. This led to the spread of diseases such as cholera.

VOCABULARY STRATEGY

What does the word *contaminated* mean in the underlined sentence? What clues can you find in the surrounding words, phrases, or sentences? Circle the words in the paragraph that could help you figure out what *contaminated* means.

The heart of the new industrial city was the factory. Working in a factory differed greatly from working on a farm. In rural villages, people worked hard, but the work varied according to the season. Some seasons were easier than others. The factory system imposed a harsh new way of life on workers. Working hours were long, with shifts lasting from twelve to sixteen hours, six or seven days a week. Exhausted workers were injured by machines that had no safety devices. Working conditions in the mines were even worse than in the factories. Factories and mines also hired many boys and girls. These children often started working at age seven or eight; a few were as young as five.

The early industrial age brought terrible hardships. In time, however, reformers pressed for laws to improve working conditions. **Labor unions** won the right to bargain with employers for better wages, hours, and working conditions. Despite the social problems created by the Industrial Revolution—low pay, dismal living conditions—the industrial age did have some positive effects. Wages rose. Also as the cost of railroad travel fell, more people could afford to travel further and faster than ever before.

READING SKILL

Understand Effects How did the Industrial Revolution affect the lives of the working class?

Harsh condition,
strict schedule
poor living conditions

Review Questions

1. What caused rapid urbanization to occur during the Industrial Revolution?

Changes in farming and soaring population growth and a demand for workers

2. How did the factory system change the way people worked?

Harsh conditions strict schedules

© Pearson Education, Inc., publishing as Pearson Prentice Hall. All rights reserved.

CHAPTER 5 SECTION 4

Note Taking Study Guide
NEW WAYS OF THINKING

Focus Question: What new ideas about economics and society were fostered as a result of the Industrial Revolution?

As you read this section in your textbook, complete the following outline to identify main ideas about the new economic and social theories.

I. **Laissez-faire economics**

   A. Adam Smith and free enterprise

      1. _____

      2. _____

II. **Malthus on population**

   A. _____

      1. _____

      2. _____

      3. _____

   B. _____

      1. _____

      2. _____

III. _____

   A. _____

      1. _____

      2. _____

IV. _____

   A. _____

      1. _____

      2. _____

   B. _____

      1. _____

      2. _____

(Outline continues on the next page.)

© Pearson Education, Inc., publishing as Pearson Prentice Hall. All rights reserved.

CHAPTER 5
SECTION 4

Note Taking Study Guide

NEW WAYS OF THINKING

(Continued from page 43)

V. _____

    A. _____

        1. _____

        2. _____

VI. _____

    A. _____

        1. _____

        2. _____

        3. _____

    B. _____

        1. _____

        2. _____

© Pearson Education, Inc., publishing as Pearson Prentice Hall. All rights reserved.

CHAPTER 5
SECTION 4

Section Summary
NEW WAYS OF THINKING

Many thinkers tried to understand the staggering changes taking place in the early Industrial Age. These thinkers looked for natural laws that governed the world of business and economics. Middle-class business leaders embraced the laissez-faire, or "hands-off" approach, believing that a free market would eventually help everyone, not just the rich. However, one British laissez-faire economist, **Thomas Malthus,** felt that the population would grow faster than the food supply. As long as the population kept growing the poor would suffer. He opposed any government help including charity and vaccinations. He urged families to have fewer children.

Other thinkers sought to modify laissez-faire ideas to justify some government intervention. The British philosopher and economist **Jeremy Bentham** advocated **utilitarianism,** or the idea that the goal of society should be the "greatest happiness for the greatest number" of citizens. Bentham's ideas influenced the British philosopher and economist John Stuart Mill. Although he strongly believed in individual freedom, Mill wanted the government to step in to improve the hard lives of the working class.

To end poverty and injustice, others offered a radical solution— **socialism.** Under socialism, the people, as a whole rather than as individuals, would own and operate the **means of production—** the farms, factories, railways, and other businesses that produced and distributed goods. A number of early socialists, such as **Robert Owen,** established communities where all work was shared and all property was owned in common. These early socialists were called Utopians.

Karl Marx, a German philosopher, formulated a new theory— a form of socialism called **communism,** in which the struggle between social classes would lead to the creation of a classless society. According to Marx, the modern class struggle pitted the bourgeoisie against the **proletariat,** or working class. In a classless, communist society, people's struggles would end because wealth and power would be equally shared. In the 1860s, Germany adapted Marx's beliefs to form a **social democracy** in which there was a gradual transition from capitalism to socialism.

Review Questions

1. Why did middle-class business leaders support laissez-faire economics?

_____

_____

2. How did utilitarians seek to modify laissez-faire ideas?

_____

_____

READING CHECK

Who were the Utopians?

_____

_____

_____

VOCABULARY STRATEGY

What does the word *formulated* mean in the underlined sentence? What clue can you find in the base word, *form*? Use the meaning of *form* to help you figure out what *formulated* means.

READING SKILL

Identify Main Ideas Explain the main ideas of Karl Marx's theory.

_____

_____

_____

© Pearson Education, Inc., publishing as Pearson Prentice Hall. All rights reserved.

CHAPTER 6
SECTION 1

Note Taking Study Guide

THE INDUSTRIAL REVOLUTION SPREADS

Focus Question: How did science, technology, and big business promote industrial growth?

As you read this section in your textbook, complete the following chart to identify main ideas about the major developments of the Industrial Revolution.

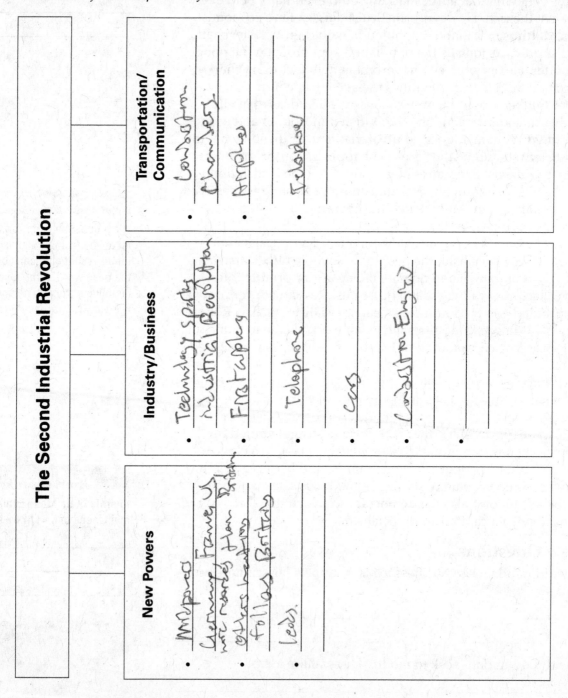

The Second Industrial Revolution

Transportation/Communication
- Combustion
- Chambers
- Amplies
- Telephone

Industry/Business
- Technology sparks industrial Revolution
- Photography
- Telephone
- Gas
- Industrial Europe

New Powers
- Improved
- Germany frames US
- not nearby than Britain
- other nations
- follows Britain
- leads

© Pearson Education, Inc., publishing as Pearson Prentice Hall. All rights reserved.

CHAPTER 6 SECTION 1

Section Summary

THE INDUSTRIAL REVOLUTION SPREADS

During the early Industrial Revolution, Britain was the world's industrial giant. Later, two new industrial powers emerged— Germany and the United States. These nations had more abundant supplies of coal, iron, and other resources than Britain. This helped them become the new industrial leaders. These nations also had the advantage of being able to follow Britain's lead, borrowing its experts and technology. The demands of an industrial society brought about many social, economic, and political changes.

Technology sparked industrial and economic growth. **Henry Bessemer** patented the process for making steel from iron. Steel became so important that industrialized countries measured their success in steel output. **Alfred Nobel** earned enough money from his invention of dynamite to fund today's Nobel prizes. Electricity replaced steam as the dominant industrial energy source. **Michael Faraday** created the first simple electric motor, as well as the first **dynamo.** In the 1870s, **Thomas Edison** made the first electric light bulb. Soon, electricity lit entire cities, the pace of city life quickened, and factories continued to operate after dark. **Interchangeable parts** and the **assembly line** made production faster and cheaper.

Technology also transformed transportation and communication. Steamships replaced sailing ships. Railroads connected cities, seaports, and industrial centers. The invention of the internal combustion engine sparked the automobile age. In the early 1900s, Henry Ford developed an assembly line to produce cars, making the United States a leader in the automobile industry. The air age began when **Orville and Wilbur Wright** flew their plane for a few seconds in 1904. Communication advances included the telegraph and telephone. **Guglielmo Marconi's** radio became the cornerstone of today's global communication network.

New technologies needed investments of large amounts of money. To get the money, owners sold **stock** to investors, growing businesses into giant **corporations.** By the late 1800s, what we call "big business" came to dominate industry. Corporations formed **cartels** to control markets.

Review Questions

1. What advantages did the new industrial powers have?

   They had more supplies of coal, iron, and other resources

2. How did the development of electricity change life in cities?

   Lit factories, quickened production, pace quickened

© Pearson Education, Inc., publishing as Pearson Prentice Hall. All rights reserved.

47

READING CHECK

What two new industrial powers emerged in the mid-1800s?

Germany &
_U.S.A._

VOCABULARY STRATEGY

What does the word *dominate* mean in the underlined sentence? It comes from a Latin word that means "lord" or "master." Use this information about the word's origin to help you figure out what *dominate* means.

READING SKILL

Identify Main Ideas How was transportation transformed during the Industrial Revolution?

Automobiles,
steamships,
railroads

CHAPTER 6 SECTION 2

Note Taking Study Guide

THE RISE OF THE CITIES

Focus Question: How did the Industrial Revolution change life in the cities?

As you read this section in your textbook, complete the following outline to identify main ideas and supporting details about how the Industrial Revolution changed life in the cities.

I. Medicine and the population explosion

   A. The fight against disease

      1. Louis Pasteur develops vaccines and pasteurization

      2. Koch Robert bacteria

   B. Life in the city Hospital care improve

      1. Landscape changes Nightingale - sanitary measure

      2. Rich live on outskirts, poor het in cities

II. Life care improve Life in the cities

   A. City landscape design

      1. City planners design the layout of cities

      2. Rich live on outskirts, poor in cities

   B. sidewalks, sewers and skyscrapers

      1. streets & tunnels

      2. steel create skyscrapers

   C. Slum conditions

      1. crowdy

      2. crime

   D. The lure of the city

      1. attracts by work education

      2. attracts by entertainment

III. Working class struggle

   A. Labor union

      1. workers strike to protest conditions

      2. Government pass laws to improve conditions

   B. standards of living

      1. Wage gaps between skilled and unskilled

      2. the quality are available

© Pearson Education, Inc., publishing as Pearson Prentice Hall. All rights reserved.

Section Summary

CHAPTER 6 SECTION 2

THE RISE OF THE CITIES

Between 1800 and 1900, the population of Europe more than doubled. Advances in medicine slowed death rates and caused a population explosion. In the fight against disease, scientists speculated about a **germ theory**. They believed that certain germs might cause specific diseases. In 1870, French chemist **Louis Pasteur** showed that this link is real. Ten years later, German doctor **Robert Koch** identified the bacteria that causes tuberculosis, a deadly respiratory disease. As people began to understand how germs cause diseases, they practiced better hygiene. This helped decrease the number of deaths from disease. Better hygiene also led to improvements in hospital care. British nurse and reformer **Florence Nightingale** introduced sanitary measures in hospitals. The English surgeon **Joseph Lister** discovered how antiseptics prevent infection.

As industrialization progressed, city life underwent dramatic changes in Europe and the United States. The most extensive **urban renewal** took place in Paris in the 1850s. Wide boulevards, paved streets, and splendid public buildings replaced old streets full of tenement housing. Architects used steel to build soaring buildings called skyscrapers. Electric streetlights illuminated the night, increasing safety. Massive new sewage systems in London and Paris provided cleaner water and better sanitation, sharply cutting death rates from disease.

Despite these efforts, urban life remained difficult for the poor. In the worst tenements, whole families were often crammed into a single room. Slums remained a fact of city life. Still, millions of people were attracted to cities because of the promise of work, entertainment, and educational opportunities.

However, industrialization and urban improvements did not improve conditions for workers. Most experienced low wages, long hours, unsafe environments, and the constant threat of unemployment. Workers protested these terrible conditions. They formed **mutual-aid societies** and organized unions. Pressured by unions, reformers, and working-class voters, governments passed laws to regulate working conditions. Wages varied, but overall, the **standard of living** for most workers did rise.

Review Questions

1. How did advances in medicine cause a population explosion?

   It helped decrease the number of deaths used by disease

2. What two changes in the 1800s made city life safer and healthier?

   Electric street lights lights the light / new sewese systems.

READING CHECK

What did Louis Pasteur do in 1870?

certain germs light cause disease Discovred cell

VOCABULARY STRATEGY

What does the word *illuminated* mean in the underlined sentence? The root of this word is from *lumen*, which is Latin for "light." How can you use the root of *illuminated* to help you figure out its meaning?

READING SKILL

Identify Supporting Details In what ways were working conditions difficult for most industrial workers?

crowded long hours unsafe environments

© Pearson Education, Inc., publishing as Pearson Prentice Hall. All rights reserved.

Note Taking Study Guide

CHANGING ATTITUDES AND VALUES

CHAPTER 6 SECTION 3

Focus Question: How did the Industrial Revolution change the old social order and long-held traditions in the Western world?

As you read this section in your textbook, complete the following table. List new issues that caused change in the first column and identify two supporting details for each in the second column.

Changes in Social Order and Values	
Issue	**Change**
• New social order	• Upper class: old nobility, new industrialists, business families • •
• Rights for women	• •
•	• •
•	• •
•	• •

© Pearson Education, Inc., publishing as Pearson Prentice Hall. All rights reserved.

CHAPTER 6 SECTION 3

Section Summary
CHANGING ATTITUDES AND VALUES

In the late 1800s, the social order in the Western world slowly changed. Instead of nobles and peasants, a more complex social structure emerged, made up of three classes. The new upper class included very rich business families. Below this tiny elite were a growing middle class and a struggling lower middle class. Workers and peasants were at the bottom of the social ladder.

The middle class developed its own values and way of life, which included a strict code of rules that dictated behavior for every occasion. A **cult of domesticity** also emerged that idealized women and the home.

Demands for women's rights also challenged the traditional social order. Across Europe and the United States, many women campaigned for fairness in marriage, divorce, and property laws. Many women's groups also supported the **temperance movement.** In the United States, reformers such as **Elizabeth Cady Stanton** and **Sojourner Truth** were dedicated to achieving **women's suffrage.**

Industrialized societies recognized the need for a literate workforce. Reformers persuaded many governments to require basic education for all children and to set up public schools. More and more children attended school, and public education improved.

At the same time, new ideas in science challenged long-held beliefs. **John Dalton** developed the modern atomic theory. <u>The most controversial new idea, however, came from the British naturalist</u> <u>Charles Darwin.</u> His ideas upset those who debated the validity of his conclusions. Darwin argued that all forms of life had evolved over millions of years. His theory of natural selection explained the long, slow process of evolution. In natural selection, members of each species compete to survive. Unfortunately, some people applied Darwin's theory of natural selection to encourage **racism.** Others applied his ideas to economic competition.

Religion continued to be a major force in Western society. The grim realities of industrial life stirred feelings of compassion and charity. For example, the **social gospel** urged Christians to push for reforms in housing, healthcare, and education.

Review Questions

1. How did the social structure change in the late 1800s?

_3 classes _ _upperclass _ middle class_
lower middle class?

2. For what rights did women in Europe and the United States campaign?

They campaigned for the right to vote

READING CHECK

What new scientific theory did Charles Darwin promote to explain evolution?

Natural
selection

VOCABULARY STRATEGY

What does the word *controversial* mean in the underlined sentence? Use context clues, or surrounding words and sentences, to figure out what *controversial* means.

READING SKILL

Identify Supporting Details
What changes in education were brought about by the Industrial Revolution?

basic education
made by government

© Pearson Education, Inc., publishing as Pearson Prentice Hall. All rights reserved.

Note Taking Study Guide
ARTS IN THE INDUSTRIAL AGE

Focus Question: What artistic movements emerged in reaction to the Industrial Revolution?

As you read this section in your textbook, complete the following table. Identify supporting details about the major features of the artistic movements of the 1800s.

Major Artistic Movements of the 1800s		
Movement	**Goals/Characteristics**	**Major Figures**

Romanticism	• Rebellion against reason
	• Emphasis on imagination
	  freedom / emotion.
	• Romantic hero in
	  literature
	• Architecture on glory
	• Past, music that
	  stirs the feeling
	• Use of direct
	  language
		• William Wordsworth
		• William Blake
		• Samuel Taylor Coleridge
		• Lord Byron
		• Victor Hugo
		• Ludwig van Beethoven
		• Charlotte Brontë
		• Eugène Delacroix

Realism	• To represent world as is
	  w/o any flaw
	• Focus on harsh side
	  of life
	• Novel depicted grim
	  realities
	• Plays bring real life to
	  stage
	• Painters focused on
	  ordinary subjects
		• Major figures?
		• Charles Dickens,
		  Victor Hugo,
		  Henrik
		  Ibsen, Thomas
		• Gustave
		  Courbet!

Impressionism	• To capture first fleeting
	  impression on viewers eye
	• Movement made in
	  realism art reaction to photo
		• Claude Monet
		• Edgar Degas

Post Impressionism	• variety of styles	• George Seurat • Vincent van Gogh • Paul Gauguin

© Pearson Education, Inc., publishing as Pearson Prentice Hall. All rights reserved.

CHAPTER 6 SECTION 4

Section Summary
ARTS IN THE INDUSTRIAL AGE

From about 1750 to 1850, a cultural movement called **romanticism** emerged in Western art and literature. The movement was a reaction against the rationality and restraint of the Enlightenment. Romanticism emphasized imagination, freedom, and emotion. In contrast to Enlightenment literature, the works of romantic writers included direct language, intense feelings, and a glorification of nature.

Poets **William Wordsworth, William Blake,** and **Lord Byron** were among the major figures of the romantic movement. Romantic novelists, such as **Victor Hugo,** were inspired by history, legend, and folklore. Romantic composers also tried to stir deep emotions. The passionate music of **Ludwig van Beethoven** combined classical forms with a stirring range of sound. Painters, too, broke free from the formal styles of the Enlightenment. They sought to capture the beauty and power of nature with bold brush strokes and colors.

By the mid-1800s, another new artistic movement, **realism,** took hold in the West. Realists sought to represent the world as it was, without romantic sentiment. Their works made people aware of the grim conditions of the Industrial Age. Many realists wanted to improve the lives of those they depicted. **Charles Dickens,** for example, vividly portrayed in his novels the lives of slum dwellers and factory workers. Some of his novels shocked middle-class readers with images of poverty, mistreatment of children, and urban crime. Painters such as **Gustave Courbet** also portrayed the realities of the time.

By the 1840s, a new art form, photography, emerged. **Louis Daguerre** produced some of the first successful photographs. Some artists questioned the effectiveness of realism when a camera could make such exact images. By the 1870s, one group had started a new art movement, **impressionism.** Impressionists, such as **Claude Monet,** sought to capture the first fleeting impression made by a scene or object on the viewer's eye. By concentrating on visual impressions, rather than realism, artists created a fresh view of familiar subjects. Later painters, called postimpressionists, developed a variety of styles. **Vincent van Gogh,** for example, experimented with sharp brush lines and bright colors.

Review Questions

1. How did the romantic movement differ from the Enlightenment?
   It included direct language, feeling and history

2. What was the goal of the impressionist artists?
   To show the real world

© Pearson Education, Inc., publishing as Pearson Prentice Hall. All rights reserved.

READING CHECK

Against what was the romantic movement a reaction?
against rationality and restraint

VOCABULARY STRATEGY

What does the word *intense* mean in the underlined sentence? What clues can you find in the surrounding words, phrases, or sentences that might have a similar meaning? Use these context clues to help you learn what *intense* means.

READING SKILL

Identify Supporting Details
Identify two supporting details for the following main idea: The artists of the realism movement made people more aware of the harsh conditions of life in the Industrial Age.
It showed the

CHAPTER 7 SECTION 1

Note Taking Study Guide

BUILDING A GERMAN NATION

Focus Question: How did Otto von Bismarck, the chancellor of Prussia, lead the drive for German unity?

As you read this section in your textbook, complete the following chart to record the sequence of events that led to German unification.

Napoleon raids German lands.

© Pearson Education, Inc., publishing as Pearson Prentice Hall. All rights reserved.

Section Summary

CHAPTER 7 SECTION 1

BUILDING A GERMAN NATION

In the early 1800s, German-speaking people lived in a number of German states. Many also lived in Prussia and the Austrian empire. There was no unified German nation. However, events unfolded in the mid-nineteenth century that eventually led to the formation of one Germany. Between 1806 and 1812, Napoleon invaded these lands. He organized a number of German states into the Rhine Confederation. After Napoleon's defeat, the Congress of Vienna created the German Confederation. This was a weak alliance of German states headed by Austria. In the 1830s, Prussia created an economic union called the *Zollverein*. This union removed tariff barriers between many German states, yet they remained politically fragmented.

Otto von Bismarck, the **chancellor** of Prussia, led the drive to unite the German states—but under Prussian rule. Bismarck was a master of **Realpolitik,** or realistic politics based on the needs of the state. After creating a powerful military, he was ready to pursue an aggressive foreign policy. Over the next decade, Bismarck led Prussia into three wars. Each war increased Prussian power and paved the way for German unity.

In 1866, Bismarck created an excuse to attack Austria. The Austro-Prussian War lasted only seven weeks. Afterwards, Prussia **annexed** several north German states. In France, the Prussian victory angered Napoleon III. A growing rivalry between the two nations led to the Franco-Prussian War of 1870. Bismarck worsened the crisis by rewriting and releasing to the press a telegram that reported on a meeting between William I of Prussia and the French ambassador. Bismarck's editing of the telegram made it seem that William I had insulted the Frenchman. Furious, Napoleon III declared war on Prussia, as Bismarck had hoped. The Prussian army quickly defeated the French.

Delighted by the victory, German princes persuaded William I to take the title **kaiser** of Germany. In January 1871, German nationalists celebrated the birth of the Second **Reich.** Bismarck drafted a constitution that created a two-house legislature. Even so, the real power was in the hands of the kaiser and Bismarck.

Review Questions

1. What events occurred in the early 1800s that helped promote German unity?

   Napoleons war, Zollverein, and the
   German Confederation.

2. How did Bismarck use war to create a united Germany under Prussian rule?

   He used war by unifying the German
   states, the empire grew after war

READING CHECK

What was Realpolitik?

realistic policy
based on the
needs of the state

VOCABULARY STRATEGY

What does the word *editing* mean in the underlined sentence? Circle the context clues in the paragraph that could help you figure out what *editing* means.

READING SKILL

Recognize Sequence What events led Napoleon III to declare war on Prussia?

Bismarck sent a
false telegram
insulting France.

© Pearson Education, Inc., publishing as Pearson Prentice Hall. All rights reserved.

Note Taking Study Guide
GERMANY STRENGTHENS

Focus Question: How did Germany increase its power after unifying in 1871?

As you read this section in your textbook, complete the following chart to record the causes and effects of a strong German nation.

Effects

- Industrial development

Strong German Nation

Causes

- Abundant natural resources

© Pearson Education, Inc., publishing as Pearson Prentice Hall. All rights reserved.

Section Summary
GERMANY STRENGTHENS

After unification in 1871, the new German empire emerged as an industrial giant. Several factors made industrialization in Germany possible, such as ample iron and coal resources. These are the basic ingredients for industrial development. A disciplined and educated workforce also helped the economy grow. The German middle class created a productive and efficient society that prided itself on its sense of responsibility. Additionally, a growing population provided a huge home market for goods and a large supply of industrial workers.

German industrialists recognized the value of applied science in developing new products, such as synthetic chemicals and dyes. Both industrialists and the government supported scientific research and development. The government also promoted economic development. It issued a single form of currency for Germany and reorganized the banking system. The leaders of the new empire were determined to maintain economic strength as well as military power.

Bismarck pursued several foreign-policy goals. He wanted to keep France weak and build strong links with Austria and Russia. On the domestic front, Bismarck, called "the Iron Chancellor," targeted the Catholic Church and the Socialists. He believed these groups posed a threat to the new German state. He thought Catholics would be more loyal to the Church than to Germany. He also worried that Socialists would undermine the loyalty of workers and turn them toward revolution. Bismarck tried to repress both groups, but his efforts failed. For example, the *Kulturkampf* was a set of laws intended to weaken the role of the Church. Instead, the faithful rallied to support the Church. When repressing the Socialists failed to work, Bismarck changed course and pioneered social reform.

In 1888, **William II** became the kaiser. He believed that his right to rule came from God, and he shocked Europe by asking Bismarck to resign. Not surprisingly, William II resisted efforts to introduce democratic reforms. However, his government provided many **social welfare** programs to help certain groups of people. The government also provided services such as cheap transportation and electricity.

Review Questions

1. What did the German government do to promote economic development?

   New products, science, synthetic chemicals & dyes

2. Why did Bismarck believe Catholics posed a threat to the new German state?

   He thought they would be more loyal to Church

READING CHECK

What two ingredients are basic for industrial development?

Iron and Coal

VOCABULARY STRATEGY

What does the word *synthetic* mean in the underlined sentence? Notice that these chemicals and dyes did not appear in nature, but were developed. Using this clue, write a definition for *synthetic*.

READING SKILL

Recognize Sequence Correctly number the following events:

3 William II becomes Kaiser.

2 Germany unifies in 1871.

1 Government reorganizes the banking system.

4 Bismarck is asked to resign.

© Pearson Education, Inc., publishing as Pearson Prentice Hall. All rights reserved.

Focus Question: How did influential leaders help create a unified Italy?

As you read this section in your textbook, complete the following timeline to show the sequence of events that led to Italian unification.

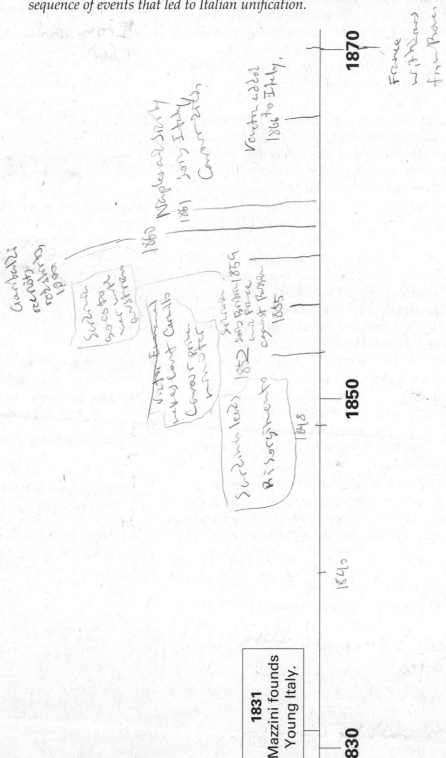

1870

France withdraws from Rome.

Venetia added to Italy. 1866

Naples and Sicily join Italy. Cavour sent 1861

1860

Garibaldi recruits 1860

Sardinia defeats Austria

Victor Emanuel II and Count Camillo Cavour's reforms

Sardinia joins Britain 1854 and France against Russia 1855

Sardinia leads 1852 Risorgimento

1848

1850

1840

1831
Mazzini founds
Young Italy.

1830

© Pearson Education, Inc., publishing as Pearson Prentice Hall. All rights reserved.

CHAPTER 7 · SECTION 3

Section Summary
UNIFYING ITALY

The peoples of the Italian peninsula had not been unified since Roman times. By the early 1800s, however, patriots were determined to build a new, united Italy. As in Germany, Napoleon's invasions had sparked dreams of nationalism.

In the 1830s, the nationalist leader Giuseppe Mazzini founded Young Italy. <u>The goal of this secret society was "to constitute Italy, one, free, independent, republican nation." To nationalists like Mazzini, establishing a unified Italy made sense because of geography and a common language and history.</u> It also made economic sense because it would end trade barriers among Italian states. Unification would stimulate industry, too.

Victor Emmanuel II, the constitutional monarch of Sardinia, hoped to join other states with his own and increase his power. In 1852, he made Count **Camillo Cavour** his prime minister. Cavour's long-term goal was to end Austrian power in Italy. With help from France, Sardinia defeated Austria and annexed Lombardy. Meanwhile, nationalist groups overthrew Austrian-backed leaders in other northern Italian states. In the south, **Giuseppe Garibaldi** had recruited a force of 1,000 red-shirted volunteers. He and his "Red Shirts" quickly won control of Sicily. Then they crossed to the mainland and marched triumphantly to Naples. Garibaldi turned over both regions to Victor Emmanuel. In 1861, Victor Emmanuel II was crowned king of Italy. Only Rome and Venetia remained outside the nation. During the Franco-Prussian War, however, France was forced to withdraw its troops from Rome. Additionally, Italy acquired Venetia in a deal with Bismarck after the Austro-Prussian War. For the first time since the fall of the Roman empire, Italy was a united land.

However, Italy faced many problems as **anarchists** and radicals struggled against the conservative government. Tensions grew between the north and south. The north was richer and had more cities. The south was poor and rural. Still, Italy developed economically and the population grew. For many, however, **emigration** offered a chance to improve their lives. Large numbers of Italians left for the United States, Canada, and Latin America.

Review Questions

1. Why did nationalists feel that a unified Italy made sense?

   Geography and common language &
   history.

2. Why did tensions between the north and south grow after unification?

   North; richer, more cities
   South, poorer, rural.

READING CHECK

What was Camillo Cavour's long-term goal as prime minister?

End Austrian
power in Italy.

VOCABULARY STRATEGY

What does the word *constitute* mean in the first underlined sentence? Note that the word is a verb, which means it describes an action. Read the second underlined sentence to find out what action the nationalists wanted to take. Use this information to help you figure out what *constitute* means.

READING SKILL

Recognize Sequence What events took place between Garibaldi's recruitment of the "Red Shirts" and Victor Emmanuel II's crowning as king of Italy?

Won control of
Sicily and Naples.

© Pearson Education, Inc., publishing as Pearson Prentice Hall. All rights reserved.

Focus Question: How did the desire for national independence among ethnic groups weaken and ultimately destroy the Austrian and Ottoman empires?

As you read this section in your textbook, complete the following table to record some major events in Austrian history during the 1800s.

Events in Austrian History	
1840	Factories springing up (by workers) → low pay → Poor conditions — Pay
1848	National revolts broke out throughout the government
1859	Austria defeated by France and Sardinia
1866	Austria defeated in war with Prussia
1867	Dual monarchy between Austria and Hungary

© Pearson Education, Inc., publishing as Pearson Prentice Hall. All rights reserved.

Section Summary
NATIONALISM THREATENS OLD EMPIRES

In 1800, the Hapsburgs of Austria, the oldest ruling house in Europe, presided over a multinational empire. The emperor, Francis I, upheld conservative goals against growing liberal forces. He could not, however, hold back the changes that were happening throughout Europe. By the 1840s, Austria was facing the problems of industrial life, including growth of cities, worker discontent, and socialism. Nationalists were threatening the old order. The Hapsburgs ignored these demands for change and crushed revolts. Amid the turmoil, 18-year-old **Francis Joseph** inherited the Hapsburg throne. He granted some limited reforms, such as adopting a constitution. The reforms, however, satisfied only the German-speaking Austrians, but none of the other ethnic groups.

Austria's defeat in the 1866 war with Prussia brought even more pressure for change, especially from Hungarians within the empire. **Ferenc Deák** helped work out a compromise known as the **Dual Monarchy** of Austria-Hungary. Under this agreement, Austria and Hungary became separate states. Each had its own constitution, but Francis Joseph ruled both—as emperor of Austria and king of Hungary. However, other groups within the empire resented this arrangement. Restlessness increased among various Slavic groups. Some nationalist leaders called on Slavs to unite in "fraternal solidarity." By the early 1900s, nationalist unrest left the government paralyzed in the face of pressing political and social problems.

Like the Hapsburgs, the Ottomans ruled a multinational empire. It stretched from Eastern Europe and the Balkans to the Middle East and North Africa. As in Austria, nationalist demands tore at the fabric of the Ottoman empire. During the 1800s, various peoples revolted, hoping to set up their own independent states. With the empire weakened, European powers scrambled to divide up Ottoman lands. A complex web of competing interests led to a series of crises and wars in the Balkans. Russia fought several wars against the Ottomans. France and Britain sometimes joined the Russians, and sometimes the Ottomans. By the early 1900s, observers were referring to the region as the "Balkan powder keg." The "explosion" came in 1914 and helped set off World War I.

Review Questions

1. What problems threatened the Hapsburg empire in the 1840s?

_____

_____

2. What effect did nationalist unrest have on the Ottoman empire?

_____

_____

READING CHECK

What new political entity did Ferenc Deák help create?

_____

_____

_____

VOCABULARY STRATEGY

What does the word *fraternal* mean in the underlined sentence? The word derives from the Latin word *frater*, which means "brother." Use this information about the word's origin to help you figure out what *fraternal* means.

READING SKILL

Recognize Sequence What are two events that led to the decline of the Austrian empire in the late 1800s?

1. _____

_____

2. _____

© Pearson Education, Inc., publishing as Pearson Prentice Hall. All rights reserved.

CHAPTER 7 SECTION 5

Note Taking Study Guide
RUSSIA: REFORM AND REACTION

Focus Question: Why did industrialization and reform come more slowly to Russia than to Western Europe?

As you read this section in your textbook, complete the following timeline to show the sequence of events in Russia during the late 1800s and early 1900s.

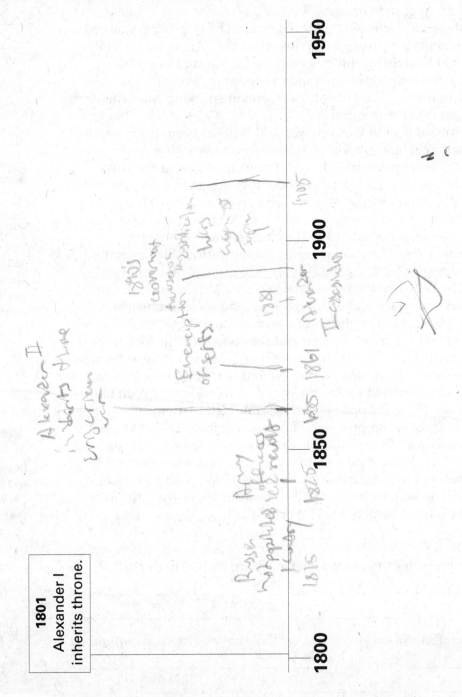

1801
Alexander I inherits throne.

© Pearson Education, Inc., publishing as Pearson Prentice Hall. All rights reserved.

CHAPTER 7 SECTION 5

Section Summary

RUSSIA: REFORM AND REACTION

By 1815, Russia was the largest, most populous nation in Europe. The Russian **colossus** had immense natural resources. Reformers hoped to free Russia from autocratic rule, economic backwardness, and social injustice. One of the obstacles to progress was the rigid social structure. Another was that, for centuries, tsars had ruled with absolute power, while the majority of Russians were poor serfs.

Alexander II became tsar in 1855 during the **Crimean War.** Events in his reign represent the pattern of reform and repression of previous tsars. The war, which ended in a Russian defeat, revealed the country's backwardness and inefficient bureaucracy. People demanded changes, so Alexander II agreed to some reforms. He ordered the **emancipation** of the serfs. He also set up a system of local, elected assemblies called **zemstvos.** Then he introduced legal reforms, such as trial by jury. These reforms, however, failed to satisfy many Russians. <u>Radicals pressed for even greater changes and more reforms.</u> The tsar then backed away from reform and moved toward repression. This sparked anger among radicals and, in 1881, terrorists assassinated Alexander II. In response to his father's death, Alexander III revived harsh, repressive policies. He also suppressed the cultures of non-Russian peoples, which led to their persecution. Official persecution encouraged **pogroms,** or violent mob attacks on Jewish people. Many left Russia and became **refugees.**

Russia began to industrialize under Alexander III and his son Nicholas II. However, this just increased political and social problems because nobles and peasants feared the changes industrialization brought. News of military disasters added to the unrest. On Sunday, January 22, 1905, a peaceful protest calling for reforms turned deadly when the tsar's troops killed and wounded hundreds of people. In the months that followed this "Bloody Sunday," discontent exploded across Russia. Nicholas was forced to make sweeping reforms. He agreed to summon a **Duma.** He then appointed a new prime minister, **Peter Stolypin.** Stolypin soon realized Russia needed reform, not just repression. Unfortunately, the changes he introduced were too limited. By 1914, Russia was still an autocracy, but the nation was simmering with discontent.

Review Questions

1. What effect did the Crimean War have on Russia?

_____

_____

2. What happened on January 22, 1905?

_____

_____

READING CHECK

What were zemstvos?

_____

_____

_____

VOCABULARY STRATEGY

What does the word *radicals* mean in the underlined sentence? Think about why these people were dissatisfied with Alexander II's reforms. Circle the words in the underlined sentence that help you figure out what *radical* means.

READING SKILL

Recognize Sequence What happened between Alexander II's becoming tsar and his assassination in 1881?

_____

_____

_____

© Pearson Education, Inc., publishing as Pearson Prentice Hall. All rights reserved.

Note Taking Study Guide
DEMOCRATIC REFORM IN BRITAIN

Focus Question: How did political reform gradually expand suffrage and make the British Parliament more democratic during the 1800s?

As you read this section in your textbook, complete the outline below to identify the main ideas in the section.

I. Reforming Parliament

    A. Reformers press for change.

        1. _____

        2. _____

    B. _____

        1. _____

        2. _____

        3. _____

    C. _____

        1. _____

        2. _____

II. _____

    A. _____

        1. _____

        2. _____

    B. _____

        1. _____

        2. _____

III. _____

    A. _____

        1. _____

        2. _____

        3. _____

    B. _____

        1. _____

        2. _____

© Pearson Education, Inc., publishing as Pearson Prentice Hall. All rights reserved.

CHAPTER 8 SECTION 1

Section Summary
DEMOCRATIC REFORM IN BRITAIN

In 1815, Britain was governed by a constitutional monarchy with a Parliament and two political parties. However, it was far from democratic. The House of Commons, although elected, was controlled by wealthy nobles and squires. The House of Lords could veto any bill passed by the House of Commons. Catholics and non-Church of England Protestants could not vote. **Rotten boroughs,** rural towns that had lost most of their voters during the Industrial Revolution, still sent members to Parliament. At the same time, new industrial cities had no seats allocated in Parliament.

The Great Reform Act of 1832 redistributed seats in the House of Commons, giving representation to new cities and eliminating rotten boroughs. It enlarged the **electorate** but kept a property requirement for voting. Protesters known as the Chartists demanded universal male suffrage, annual parliamentary elections, salaries for members of Parliament, and a **secret ballot.** In time, most of the reforms they proposed were passed by Parliament.

From 1837 to 1901, the great symbol in British life was **Queen Victoria.** She set the tone for the Victorian age that was named for her. She embodied the values of duty, thrift, honesty, hard work, and respectability. Under Victoria, the middle class felt confident. That confidence grew as the British empire expanded.

In the 1860s, a new era dawned in British politics. **Benjamin Disraeli** forged the Tories into the modern Conservative Party. The Whigs, led by **William Gladstone,** evolved into the Liberal Party. Disraeli and Gladstone alternated as prime minister and fought for important reforms. The Conservative Party pushed through the Reform Bill of 1867, which gave the vote to many working-class men. In the 1880s, the Liberals got the vote extended to farm workers and most other men.

By century's end, Britain had truly transformed from a constitutional monarchy to a **parliamentary democracy.** In this form of government, executive leaders are chosen by and responsible to the parliament, and they are members of it. In 1911, measures were passed that restricted the power of the House of Lords, and it eventually became a largely ceremonial body.

Review Questions

1. What was the result of the Great Reform Act of 1832?

_____

_____

2. How is a parliamentary democracy organized?

_____

_____

READING CHECK

What are rotten boroughs?

_____

_____

_____

VOCABULARY STRATEGY

What does the word *allocated* mean in the underlined sentence? Note that the Great Reform Act of 1832 corrected the problem described in this sentence by "redistributing" seats in the House of Commons. Use this context clue to help you understand the meaning of the word *allocated*.

READING SKILL

Identify Main Ideas What is the main idea in the first paragraph of the Summary?

_____

_____

_____

© Pearson Education, Inc., publishing as Pearson Prentice Hall. All rights reserved.

CHAPTER 8 SECTION 2

Note Taking Study Guide
SOCIAL AND ECONOMIC REFORM IN BRITAIN

Focus Question: What social and economic reforms were passed by the British Parliament during the 1800s and early 1900s?

As you read this section in your textbook, complete the chart below by listing reforms in Britain during the 1800s and early 1900s.

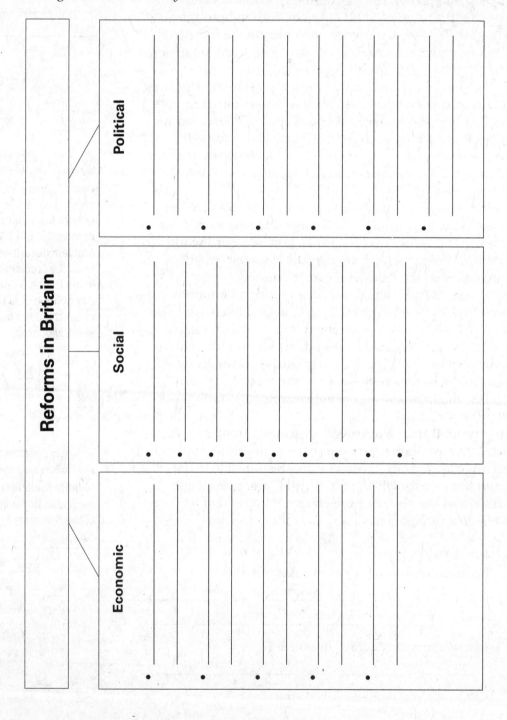

© Pearson Education, Inc., publishing as Pearson Prentice Hall. All rights reserved.

Name_____ Class_____ Date_____

During the 1800s, the British Parliament passed important laws. One issue was **free trade,** or trade without restrictions between countries. The Corn Laws caused fierce debate. These laws imposed high tariffs on imported grain. Farmers and landowners benefited, but the tariffs made bread more expensive. In 1846, Parliament **repealed** the Corn Laws. Another important reform, brought about by the **abolition movement,** was the end of the slave trade in 1807. By 1833, Parliament had banned slavery in all British colonies. Other reforms reduced the number of **capital offenses,** or crimes punishable by death. Instead of being put to death, many petty criminals were transported to **penal colonies** in Australia and New Zealand.

Working conditions in the industrial age were grim and often dangerous. Gradually, Parliament passed laws to regulate conditions in factories and mines. Other laws set minimum wages and maximum hours of work. Trade unions became legal in 1825 and worked to improve the lives of their members. Both the Liberal and Conservative parties enacted reforms to benefit workers, including free elementary education. The Labour Party, formed in 1900, soon became one of Britain's major parties. In the early 1900s, Parliament passed laws to protect workers with old-age pensions and accident, health, and unemployment insurance.

During this time, women struggled for the right to vote. When mass meetings and other peaceful efforts brought no results, Emmeline Pankhurst and other suffragists turned to more drastic, violent protest. They smashed windows, burned buildings, and went on hunger strikes. Not until 1918 did Parliament finally grant suffrage to women over 30.

Throughout the 1800s, Britain faced the "Irish Question." The Irish resented British rule. Many Irish peasants lived in poverty while paying high rents to **absentee landlords** living in England. Irish Catholics also had to pay tithes to the Church of England. The potato famine made problems worse. Charles Stewart Parnell and other Irish leaders argued for **home rule,** or self-government, but this was debated for decades. Under Gladstone, the government finally ended the use of Irish tithes to support the Church of England and passed laws to protect the rights of Irish tenant farmers.

Review Questions

1. Why did the Corn Laws cause fierce debate in Britain?

_____

_____

2. How did the government under Gladstone help improve conditions in Ireland?

_____

_____

READING CHECK

What are capital offenses?

_____

_____

_____

VOCABULARY STRATEGY

What does the word *drastic* mean in the underlined sentence? Note that the suffragists first tried "peaceful efforts" before turning to "more *drastic,* violent protest." The next sentence describes this. Use these context clues to help you understand what *drastic* means.

READING SKILL

Categorize Sort the laws that were passed to help workers into three categories.

_____

_____

_____

© Pearson Education, Inc., publishing as Pearson Prentice Hall. All rights reserved.

Note Taking Study Guide

CHAPTER 8 SECTION 3

DIVISION AND DEMOCRACY IN FRANCE

Focus Question: What democratic reforms were made in France during the Third Republic?

As you read this section in your textbook, complete the timeline below by labeling the main events described in this section.

© Pearson Education, Inc., publishing as Pearson Prentice Hall. All rights reserved.

CHAPTER 8 SECTION 3

Section Summary

DIVISION AND DEMOCRACY IN FRANCE

After the revolution of 1848, **Napoleon III** established the Second Empire in France. At first, he ruled like a dictator. In the 1860s, however, he lifted some censorship and gave the legislature more power. He promoted investment in industry and ventures such as railroad building. During this period, a French entrepreneur organized the building of the **Suez Canal** in Egypt.

However, Napoleon III had major failures in foreign affairs. He tried to put the Austrian archduke Maximilian on the throne of Mexico, but Maximilian was overthrown and killed. France and Britain won the Crimean War, but France suffered terrible losses and few gains. The Franco-Prussian War was a disaster, and the Prussians captured Napoleon. He died a few years later in England.

Following Napoleon's capture, republicans established a **provisional,** or temporary, government. In 1871, an uprising broke out in Paris, and rebels set up the Paris Commune. Its goal was to save the Republic from royalists. When the rebels did not disband, the government sent troops and 20, 000 rebels were killed.

The provisional government soon became the Third Republic. Although the legislature elected a president, the **premier** had the real power. There were many political parties, and none could take control. Because of this, parties had to form **coalitions,** or alliances, to rule. Coalition governments are often unstable, and France had 50 different coalition governments in the first 10 years of the Third Republic.

A series of political scandals in the 1880s and 1890s shook public trust in the government. The most divisive scandal was the **Dreyfus affair.** Alfred Dreyfus was a Jewish army officer wrongly accused of spying for Germany. Author Émile Zola was convicted of **libel** when he charged the army and government with suppressing the truth. The affair revealed strong anti-Semitic feelings in France and led Theodor Herzl to launch modern **Zionism.**

France achieved serious reforms in the early 1900s, however. It passed labor laws regulating wages, hours, and safety conditions. Free public elementary schools were established. <u>France tried to repress Church involvement in government.</u> In 1905, it passed a law to separate church and state. Women made some gains, but they did not win the right to vote until after World War II.

Review Questions

1. What failures in foreign affairs took place under Napoleon III?

_____

_____

2. Why did French governments have to form coalitions to rule?

_____

_____

READING CHECK

What did the Dreyfus affair reveal about France?

_____

_____

_____

VOCABULARY STRATEGY

What does the word *repress* mean in the underlined sentence? Reread the sentence after the underlined sentence. What did France do to *repress* Church involvement in government? Use this context clue to help you understand the meaning of *repress*.

READING SKILL

Recognize Sequence List, in chronological order, the three French governments described in this section.

_____

_____

_____

© Pearson Education, Inc., publishing as Pearson Prentice Hall. All rights reserved.

Name_____ Class_____ Date_____

Note Taking Study Guide
EXPANSION OF THE UNITED STATES

Focus Question: How did the United States develop during the 1800s?

As you read this section in your textbook, complete the chart below by listing key events under the appropriate headings.

Civil War	
Before	**After**

• Western expansion
 	
• _____
  _____
 	
• _____
  _____
 	
• _____
  _____
	• Fifteenth Amendment extends voting rights to all adult male citizens.
	
	• _____
	  _____
	
	• _____
	  _____
	
	• _____
	  _____
	
	• _____
	  _____
	
	• _____
	  _____
	
	• _____
	  _____
	
	• _____
	  _____

© Pearson Education, Inc., publishing as Pearson Prentice Hall. All rights reserved.

Name_____ Class_____ Date_____

CHAPTER 8 SECTION 4

Section Summary

EXPANSION OF THE UNITED STATES

In the 1800s, the United States followed a policy of **expansionism,** or extending the nation's boundaries. In 1803, the **Louisiana Purchase** nearly doubled the size of the country. More territory was soon added in the West and South. Americans believed in **Manifest Destiny,** or the idea that their nation was destined to spread across the entire continent.

Voting, slavery, and women's rights were important issues at this time. In 1800, only white men who owned property could vote. By the 1830s, most white men had the right to vote. William Lloyd Garrison, Frederick Douglass, and other abolitionists called for an end to slavery. Lucretia Mott, Elizabeth Cady Stanton, Susan B. Anthony, and others began to seek equality.

Economic differences, as well as slavery, divided the country into the North and the South. When Abraham Lincoln was elected in 1860, most Southern states **seceded,** or withdrew, from the Union. The American Civil War soon began. Southerners fought fiercely, but the North had more people, more industry, and more resources. The South finally surrendered in 1865.

During the war, Lincoln issued the Emancipation Proclamation, which declared that the slaves in the South were free. After the war, slavery was banned throughout the nation, and African Americans were granted some political rights. However, African Americans still faced restrictions, including **segregation,** or legal separation, in public places. Some state laws prevented African Americans from voting.

After the Civil War, the United States became the world leader in industrial and agricultural production. By 1900, giant monopolies controlled whole industries. For example, John D. Rockefeller's Standard Oil Company dominated the world's petroleum industry. Big business enjoyed huge profits, but not everyone shared in the prosperity. Reformers tried to address this problem. Unions sought better wages and working conditions for factory workers. Farmers and city workers formed the Populist Party to seek changes. Progressives sought to ban child labor, limit working hours, regulate monopolies, and give voters more power. Progressives also worked to get women the right to vote, which they did in 1920.

Review Questions

1. Why did the North win the Civil War?

_____

_____

2. How were African Americans deprived of equality after the Civil War?

_____

_____

READING CHECK

What is Manifest Destiny?

_____

_____

_____

VOCABULARY STRATEGY

What does the word *dominated* mean in the underlined sentence? Reread the sentence that precedes the underlined sentence. The Standard Oil Company was an example of the giant monopolies that "controlled" whole industries. Use this context clue to help you understand the meaning of the word *dominated.*

READING SKILL

Categorize Categorize the reforms discussed in this Summary by the group that did or would benefit from them.

_____

_____

_____

© Pearson Education, Inc., publishing as Pearson Prentice Hall. All rights reserved.

Focus Question: How did Western nations come to dominate much of the world in the late 1800s?

As you read this section in your textbook, complete the chart below with the multiple causes of imperialism in the 1800s.

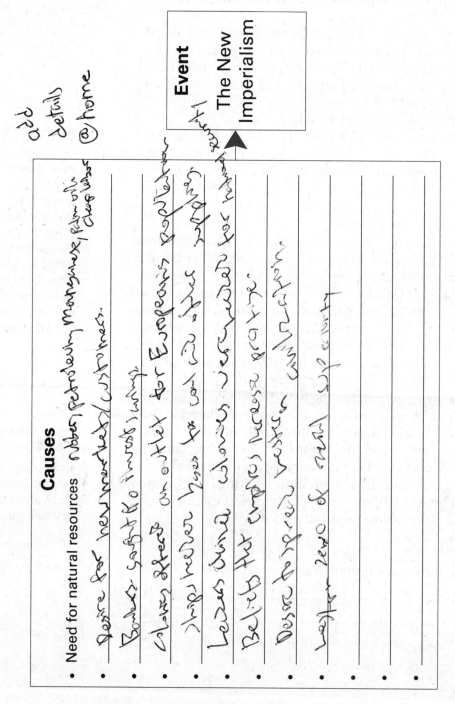

Event

The New Imperialism

add details @ home

Causes

- Need for natural resources
- Desire for new markets/customers
- Bankers sought to invest savings
- Colonies often offered cheaper labor
- Leaders thought colonies were
- Beliefs that empires increase profits
- Desire to spread
-

© Pearson Education, Inc., publishing as Pearson Prentice Hall. All rights reserved.

Section Summary

BUILDING OVERSEAS EMPIRES

Many western countries built overseas empires in the late 1800s. This expansion, referred to as **imperialism,** is the domination by one country of the political, economic, or cultural life of another country or region. In the 1800s, Europeans embarked on a path of aggressive expansion called the "new imperialism." There were several causes. The Industrial Revolution was one. Manufacturers wanted access to natural resources, as well as markets for their goods. Colonies also were an outlet for Europe's growing population. Leaders claimed that colonies were needed for national security. Industrial nations seized overseas islands and harbors as bases to supply their ships.

Nationalism played an important role, too. When one European country claimed an area, rival nations would move in and claim nearby areas. Europeans felt that ruling a global empire increased a nation's prestige. Missionaries, doctors, and colonial officials believed that they had a duty to spread Western civilization. Behind the idea of the West's civilizing mission was a growing sense of racial superiority. Many Westerners used Social Darwinism to justify their domination of non-Western societies. As a result, millions of non-Westerners were robbed of their cultural heritage.

Europeans had the advantages of strong economies, well-organized governments, and powerful armies and navies. Superior technology, such as riverboats, the telegraph, and the Maxim machine gun enhanced European power. Africans and Asians tried to resist Western expansion. Some people fought the invaders. Others tried to strengthen their societies by reforming their traditions. Many organized nationalist movements to expel the imperialists.

The leading imperial powers developed several systems to control colonies. The French practiced direct rule. They sent officials and soldiers from France to run the colony. Their goal was to impose French culture on the natives. The British, by contrast, relied on indirect rule. To govern their colonies, they used local rulers. In a **protectorate,** local rulers were left in place but were expected to follow the advice of European advisors on issues such as trade or missionary activity. In a **sphere of influence,** an outside power claimed exclusive investment or trading privileges, but did not rule the area.

Review Questions

1. Which aspect of the new imperialism led to non-Westerners being robbed of their cultural heritage?

   Social Darwinism

2. What is the difference between a protectorate and a sphere of influence?

   Protectorate, rulers were left in place but expected to follow advice

   Sphere: Exclusive investment or trading privileges

   No rule

READING CHECK

How did Africans and Asians resist Western expansion?

_____

_____

_____

VOCABULARY STRATEGY

What does the word *prestige* mean in the underlined sentence? Notice that the word *increased* appears in the same sentence. What would ruling a global empire *increase* for a European nation? Use this context clue to help you figure out the meaning of *prestige.*

READING SKILL

Multiple Causes List the multiple causes of imperialism mentioned in this summary.

_____

_____

_____

© Pearson Education, Inc., publishing as Pearson Prentice Hall. All rights reserved.

CHAPTER
9
SECTION 2

Note Taking Study Guide
THE PARTITION OF AFRICA

Focus Question: How did imperialist European powers claim control over most of Africa by the end of the 1800s?

As you read this section in your textbook, complete the chart below by identifying the causes and effects of the partition of Africa by European nations.

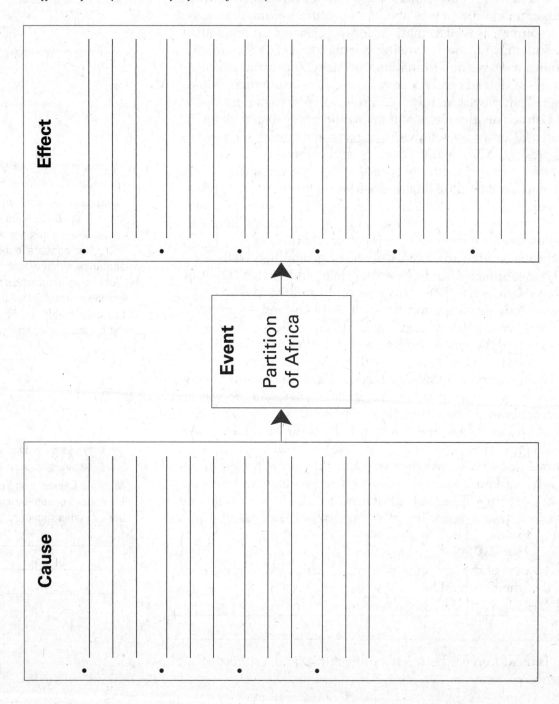

Effect

Event

Partition of Africa

Cause

© Pearson Education, Inc., publishing as Pearson Prentice Hall. All rights reserved.

CHAPTER 9 SECTION 2

Section Summary

THE PARTITION OF AFRICA

Before the scramble for colonies began in the 1800s, North Africa was under the rule of the declining Ottoman empire. West Africa experienced an Islamic revival inspired by **Usman dan Fodio.** In East Africa, port cities carried on a profitable trade. Zulus were a major force in southern Africa. A brilliant Zulu leader, **Shaka,** conquered nearby peoples. Groups driven from their homelands by the Zulus migrated north, conquering other peoples and creating powerful states.

For many years, Europeans had been trading along the African coasts. In the 1800s, contact increased as European explorers began pushing into the interior of Africa. One of the best-known was the missionary explorer **Dr. David Livingstone.** In 1869, the journalist **Henry Stanley** trekked into Africa to find Livingstone, who had not been heard from for years. Other missionaries followed explorers such as Livingstone. They built schools, churches, and medical clinics, often taking a **paternalistic** view of Africans.

About 1871, **King Leopold II** of Belgium hired Stanley to arrange trade treaties with African leaders. Leopold's action prompted Britain, France, and Germany to join in a scramble for African land. Eventually, without consulting any Africans, European leaders met in Berlin to divide the continent of Africa among themselves. In the following years, Europeans expanded further into Africa, often exploiting African people and resources. In southern Africa, the **Boer War** began when Britain wanted to claim Boer land. The Boers were descendants of Dutch farmers. The British wanted the land because gold and diamonds had been discovered there.

Africans fought back against European imperialism. In West Africa, **Samori Touré** fought French forces. **Yaa Asantewaa** was an Asante queen who led the fight against the British in West Africa. Another female leader was **Nehanda** of the Shona in Zimbabwe. In most cases resistance was not successful. However, Ethiopia was able to keep its independence. <u>Earlier, Ethiopia had been divided up among a number of rival princes who then ruled their own domains.</u> **Menelik II** modernized his country and trained an army, successfully resisting Italian invaders.

The Age of Imperialism caused a Western-educated African **elite** to emerge. Some admired Western ways. Others sought independence through nationalist movements.

Review Questions

1. Who ruled North Africa before the 1800s?

_____

_____

2. What set off a European scramble for African territories?

_____

_____

READING CHECK

Which African country was able to resist European conquest and maintain its independence?

_____

_____

_____

VOCABULARY STRATEGY

What does the word *domains* mean in the underlined sentence? Use context clues. Think about what a prince rules. What would have been divided? Use these context clues to help you figure out the meaning of *domains.*

READING SKILL

Cause and Effect What caused groups of Africans in southern Africa to migrate north? What was the effect of this?

_____

_____

_____

© Pearson Education, Inc., publishing as Pearson Prentice Hall. All rights reserved.

CHAPTER 9
SECTION 3

Note Taking Study Guide

EUROPEAN CLAIMS IN MUSLIM REGIONS

Focus Question: How did European nations extend their power into Muslim regions of the world?

As you read this section in your textbook, complete the concept web below to understand the effects of European imperialism on Muslim regions of the world.

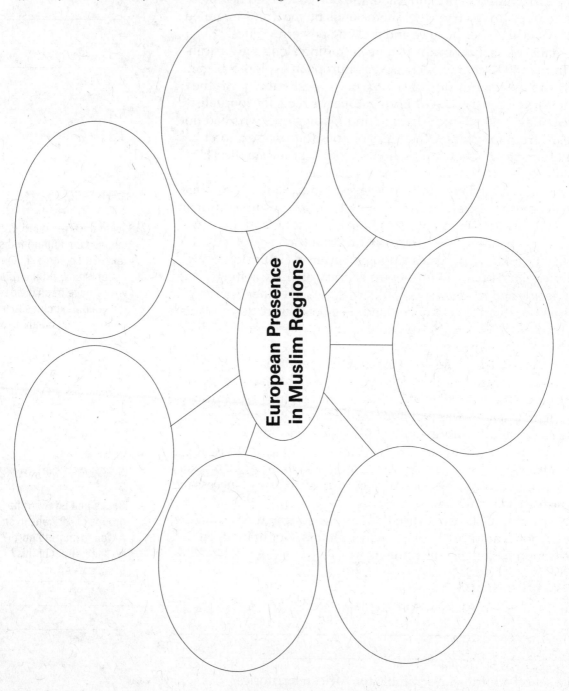

European Presence in Muslim Regions

© Pearson Education, Inc., publishing as Pearson Prentice Hall. All rights reserved.

CHAPTER 9 SECTION 3

Section Summary
EUROPEAN CLAIMS IN MUSLIM REGIONS

In the 1500s, three giant Muslim empires ruled large areas of the world—the Ottomans in the Middle East, the Safavids in Persia, and the Mughals in India. By the 1700s, all three Muslim empires were in decline, in part because of corruption and discontent. Reform movements arose, stressing religious piety and strict rules of behavior. For example, in the Sudan, **Muhammad Ahmad** announced that he was the **Mahdi,** the long-awaited savior of the faith. The Mahdi and his followers fiercely resisted British expansion into the region.

At its height, the Ottoman empire extended across North Africa, Southeastern Europe, and parts of the Middle East. Ambitious **pashas** and economic problems added to the Ottoman decline. As ideas of nationalism spread from Western Europe, internal revolts by subject peoples weakened the empire. European states took advantage of this weakness to grab Ottoman territory. Some Ottoman leaders saw the need for reform. They looked to the West for ideas on reorganizing the government and its rigid rules. In the early 1700s, they reorganized the bureaucracy and system of tax collection. However, **sultans** usually rejected reform, adding to the tension. Tension between Ottoman Turkish nationalists and minority groups led to a brutal **genocide** of Christian Armenians. Turks accused Christian Armenians of supporting Russia against the Ottoman empire.

In the early 1800s, Egypt was a semi-independent province of the Ottoman empire. **Muhammad Ali** is sometimes called the "father of modern Egypt" because he introduced a number of political and economic reforms. He also conquered the neighboring lands of Arabia, Syria, and Sudan. Before he died in 1849, he had set Egypt on the road to becoming a major Middle Eastern power. His successors were less skilled, however, and in 1882 Egypt became a protectorate of Britain.

Like the Ottoman empire, Persia—now Iran—faced major challenges. The Qajar shahs exercised absolute power. Foreign nations, especially Russia and Britain, wanted to control Iran's oil fields. They were granted **concessions** and sent troops to protect their interests. These actions outraged Iranian nationalists.

Review Questions

1. What was the extent of the Ottoman empire?

_____

_____

2. Why is Muhammad Ali sometimes called the "father of modern Egypt"?

_____

_____

READING CHECK

What were the three great Muslim empires in the 1500s?

_____

_____

_____

VOCABULARY STRATEGY

What does the word *bureaucracy* mean in the underlined sentence? *Bureau* is a French word that means "office." The suffix *-cracy* means "type of government." Use these word-origin clues to help you figure out what *bureaucracy* means.

READING SKILL

Understanding Effects What was the effect of the concessions granted to Britain and Russia in Iran?

_____

_____

_____

© Pearson Education, Inc., publishing as Pearson Prentice Hall. All rights reserved.

CHAPTER **9** SECTION 4	**Note Taking Study Guide**
	THE BRITISH TAKE OVER INDIA

Focus Question: How did Britain gradually extend its control over most of India despite opposition?

As you read this section in your textbook, complete the flowchart below to identify the causes and effects of British colonial rule in India.

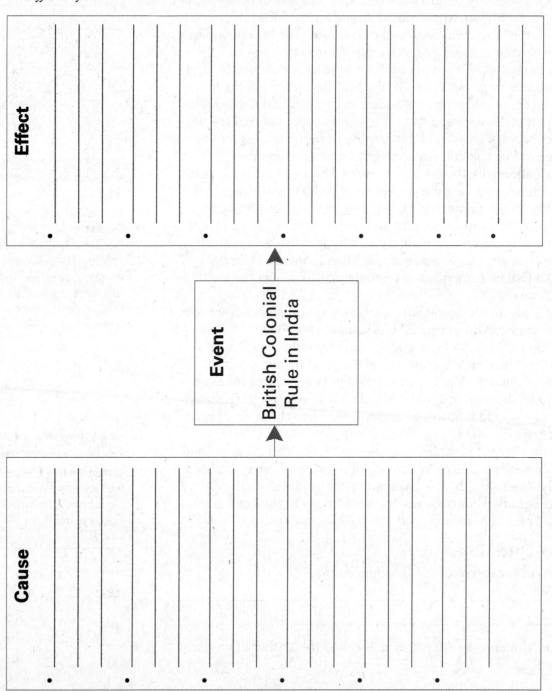

Effect

•

•

•

•

•

•

•

Event

British Colonial Rule in India

Cause

•

•

•

•

•

© Pearson Education, Inc., publishing as Pearson Prentice Hall. All rights reserved.

CHAPTER 9 SECTION 4

Section Summary

THE BRITISH TAKE OVER INDIA

Mughal rulers governed a powerful Muslim empire in India. The British East India Company had trading rights on the fringes of the Mughal empire. The main goal of the East India Company was to make money. As Mughal power declined, the East India Company extended its power. By the mid-1800s, it controlled three-fifths of India. The British were able to conquer India by exploiting its diversity, and by encouraging competition and disunity among rival princes. When necessary, the British also used force. However, British officials worked to end slavery and the caste system. They banned **sati,** a custom that called for a widow to throw herself on her husband's funeral fire. In the 1850s, the East India Company made several unpopular moves. The most serious brought about the Sepoy Rebellion. Indian soldiers, or **sepoys,** were told to bite off the tips of their rifle cartridges. This order caused a rebellion because the cartridges were greased with animal fat, violating local religious beliefs. The British crushed the revolt, killing thousands of unarmed Indians. The rebellion left a legacy of mistrust on both sides.

After the rebellion, Parliament ended the rule of the East India Company. Instead, a British **viceroy** governed India in the name of the monarch. In this way, all of Britain could benefit from trade with India as Britain incorporated India into the overall British economy. However, it remained an unequal partnership, favoring the British. Although the British built railroads and telegraph lines, they destroyed India's hand-weaving industry. Encouraging Indian farmers to grow cash crops led to massive **deforestation** and famines.

Some educated Indians urged India to follow a Western model of progress. Others felt they should keep to their own Hindu or Muslim cultures. In the early 1800s, **Ram Mohun Roy** combined both views. Roy condemned rigid caste distinctions, child marriage, sati, and **purdah,** or the isolation of women in separate quarters. He also set up educational societies to help revive pride in Indian culture. Most British disdained Indian culture and felt that Western-educated Indians would support British rule. Instead, Indians dreamed of ending British control. In 1885, Indian nationalists formed the Indian National Congress and began pressing for self-rule.

Review Questions

1. How were the British able to conquer India?

_____

_____

2. How did India benefit from Western technology?

_____

_____

READING CHECK

What was sati?

_____

_____

_____

VOCABULARY STRATEGY

What does the word *overall* mean in the underlined sentence? Notice that it is a compound word. A compound word is made from two separate words. Use the two words that make up *overall* to help you figure out what it means.

READING SKILL

Identify Causes and Effects
What caused the sepoys to rebel? What were two effects of the rebellion?

_____

_____

_____

© Pearson Education, Inc., publishing as Pearson Prentice Hall. All rights reserved.

Note Taking Study Guide

CHAPTER 9 SECTION 5

CHINA AND THE NEW IMPERIALISM

Focus Question: How did Western powers use diplomacy and war to gain power in Qing China?

As you read this section in your textbook, complete the chart below by listing the multiple causes that led to the decline of Qing China.

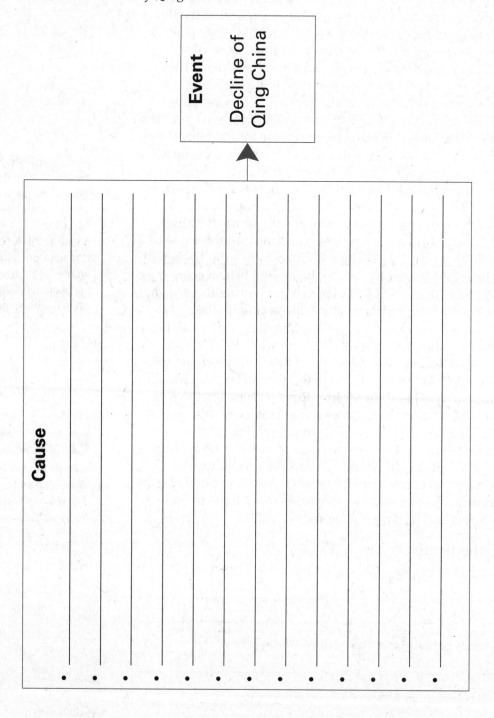

© Pearson Education, Inc., publishing as Pearson Prentice Hall. All rights reserved.

CHAPTER 9 SECTION 5

Section Summary

CHINA AND THE NEW IMPERIALISM

For centuries, China had a favorable **balance of trade,** because of a **trade surplus.** Westerners had a **trade deficit** with China, buying more from the Chinese than they sold to them. This changed in the late 1700s when the British began trading opium grown in India in exchange for Chinese tea. The Chinese government outlawed opium and called on Britain to stop this drug trade. The British refused, leading to the **Opium War** in 1839. With outdated weapons and fighting methods, the Chinese were easily defeated. Under the Treaty of Nanjing, which ended the war, Britain received a huge **indemnity** and British citizens gained the right of **extraterritoriality.** About a decade later China lost another war. France, Russia, and the United States then each made specific demands on China. <u>China was pressured to sign treaties stipulating the opening of more ports and allowing Christian missionaries in China.</u>

China also faced internal problems. Peasants hated the Qing government because of corruption. The resulting **Taiping Rebellion** against this government led to an estimated 20 million to 30 million deaths. However, the Qing government survived. In addition, the Chinese were divided over the need to adopt Western ways. Some felt Western ideas and technology threatened Confucianism. Reformers who wanted to adopt Western ways in the "self-strengthening movement" did not have government support.

Meanwhile, China's defeat in the **Sino-Japanese War** of 1894 encouraged European nations to carve out spheres of influence in China. The United States feared that American merchants might be shut out. Eventually, without consulting the Chinese, the United States insisted that Chinese trade should be open to everyone on an equal basis as part of an **Open Door Policy.** Chinese reformers blamed conservatives for not modernizing China. In 1898, the emperor, **Guang Xu,** launched the Hundred Days of Reform. Conservatives opposed this reform effort and the emperor was imprisoned.

Many Chinese, including a secret society known to Westerners as the Boxers, were angry about the presence of foreigners. Antiforeign feeling exploded in the **Boxer Uprising** in 1900. Although the Boxers failed, nationalism increased. Reformers called for a republic. One of them, **Sun Yixian,** became president of the new Chinese republic when the Qing dynasty fell in 1911.

Review Questions

1. What were the results of the Opium War?

_____

_____

2. Why was the Qing government so hated?

_____

_____

© Pearson Education, Inc., publishing as Pearson Prentice Hall. All rights reserved.

READING CHECK

Who was the Chinese reformer who became president of China in 1911?

_____

_____

VOCABULARY STRATEGY

What does the word *stipulating* mean in the underlined sentence? What clues can you find in the surrounding words, phrases, or sentences? Use these context clues to help you figure out what *stipulating* means.

READING SKILL

Recognize Multiple Causes
What brought about the Open Door Policy in China?

_____

_____

CHAPTER
10
SECTION 1

Note Taking Study Guide
JAPAN MODERNIZES

Focus Question: How did Japan become a modern industrial power, and what did it do with its new strength?

As you read this section in your textbook, complete the chart below to identify causes and effects of the Meiji Restoration.

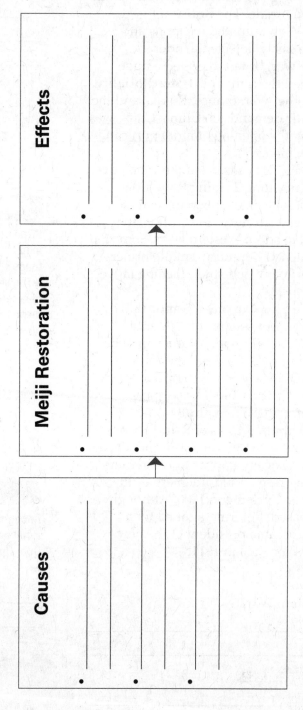

© Pearson Education, Inc., publishing as Pearson Prentice Hall. All rights reserved.

CHAPTER 10 SECTION 1 — Section Summary
JAPAN MODERNIZES

In 1603, the Tokugawa shoguns seized power in Japan and closed it to foreigners. For more than 200 years, Japan was isolated from other nations. Over time, unrest grew among many Japanese as they suffered financial hardship and lack of political power. The government responded by trying to revive old ways, emphasizing farming over commerce. These efforts had little success, and the shoguns' power weakened.

Then, in 1853, a fleet of well-armed U.S. ships led by Commodore **Matthew Perry** arrived. He demanded that Japan open its ports. Unable to defend itself, Japan was forced to sign treaties giving the United States trading and other rights. Humiliated by the terms of these unequal treaties, discontented daimyo and samurai led a revolt that unseated the shogun and placed the emperor Mutsuhito in power. Mutsuhito moved to the shogun's palace in the city of Edo, which was renamed **Tokyo,** and began a long reign known as the **Meiji Restoration.** This was a turning point in Japan's history.

The Meiji reformers wanted to create a new political and social system and build a modern industrial economy. The Meiji constitution gave all citizens equality before the law. A legislature, or **Diet,** was formed, but the emperor held absolute power. With government support, powerful banking and industrial families, known as **zaibatsu,** soon ruled over industrial empires. By the 1890s, industry was booming. Japan, a **homogeneous society,** modernized with amazing speed, partly due to its strong sense of identity.

As a small island nation, Japan lacked many resources essential for industry. Spurred by the need for natural resources and a strong ambition to equal the western imperial nations, Japan sought to build an empire. In 1876, Japan forced Korea to open its ports to Japanese trade. In 1894, competition between Japan and China in Korea led to the **First Sino-Japanese War,** which Japan easily won. Japan gained ports in China, won control over Taiwan, and joined the West in the race for empire. Ten years later, Japan successfully fought Russia in the **Russo-Japanese War.** By the early 1900s, Japan was the strongest power in Asia.

Review Questions

1. How did the Japanese respond to the unequal treaties signed with the United States?

_____

_____

2. How did the Meiji reformers try to modernize Japan?

_____

_____

READING CHECK

What helped to create a strong sense of identity in Japanese society?

_____

_____

_____

VOCABULARY STRATEGY

What does the word *emphasizing* mean in the underlined sentence? Look for context clues to its meaning in the surrounding words. Use the context clues to help you figure out what *emphasizing* means.

READING SKILL

Identify Causes and Effects What were the causes and effects of the Meiji Restoration?

_____

_____

_____

© Pearson Education, Inc., publishing as Pearson Prentice Hall. All rights reserved.

Focus Question: How did industrialized powers divide up Southeast Asia, and how did the colonized peoples react?

As you read this section, complete the flowchart below to identify causes, events, and effects of imperialism in Southeast Asia and the Pacific.

© Pearson Education, Inc., publishing as Pearson Prentice Hall. All rights reserved.

CHAPTER 10 SECTION 2

Section Summary
IMPERIALISM IN SOUTHEAST ASIA AND THE PACIFIC

By the 1700s, European merchants had gained footholds in Southeast Asia, but most of the area was still independent. In the 1800s, however, Westerners colonized much of Southeast Asia. The Dutch, for example, expanded to dominate the Dutch East Indies (now Indonesia). The British expanded from India into Burma and Malaya.

The Burmese resisted British rule and annexation but suffered disastrous defeats. The French invaded Vietnam, seeking more influence and trade markets. The Vietnamese fought fiercely but lost to superior European firepower. The French eventually took over all of Vietnam, Laos, and Cambodia and referred to these holdings as **French Indochina.** Meanwhile, the king of Siam, **Mongkut,** accepted some unequal treaties to keep Siam from becoming a European colony. By the 1890s, Europeans controlled most of Southeast Asia, where they introduced modern technology and expanded commerce and industry.

The Philippines had been under Spanish rule since the 1500s. In 1898, the **Spanish-American War** broke out. During the war, U.S. battleships destroyed the Spanish fleet stationed in the Philippines. Filipino rebel leaders declared independence and joined the Americans against Spain. In return for their help, the Filipino rebels expected the United States to recognize their independence. Instead, in the treaty that ended the war, the United States gave Spain $20 million in exchange for control of the Philippines. Bitterly disappointed, Filipinos renewed their struggle for independence, but the United States crushed the rebellion. <u>The United States, however, did promise Filipinos a gradual transition to self-rule sometime in the future.</u>

In the 1800s, the industrialized powers also began to take an interest in the Pacific islands. American sugar growers, for example, pressed for power in the Hawaiian Islands. When the Hawaiian queen **Liliuokalani** tried to reduce foreign influence, American planters overthrew her. In 1898, the United States annexed Hawaii. Supporters of annexation argued that if the United States did not take Hawaii, Britain or Japan might. By 1900, the United States, Britain, France, or Germany had claimed nearly every island in the Pacific.

Review Questions

1. How did the people of Burma and Vietnam respond to European attempts to colonize them?

_____

_____

2. Why did Filipino rebels renew their struggle for independence after the Spanish-American War?

_____

_____

READING CHECK

Which countries made up French Indochina?

_____

_____

_____

VOCABULARY STRATEGY

What does the word *transition* mean in the underlined sentence? Note that the word begins with the prefix *trans-*, which means "across or through." Use this knowledge to help you learn what the word *transition* means.

READING SKILL

Identify Causes and Effects
Identify the causes and effects of Liliuokalani's attempts to reduce foreign influence in Hawaii.

_____

_____

_____

© Pearson Education, Inc., publishing as Pearson Prentice Hall. All rights reserved.

CHAPTER 10 SECTION 3 — Note Taking Study Guide

SELF-RULE FOR CANADA, AUSTRALIA, AND NEW ZEALAND

Focus Question: How were the British colonies of Canada, Australia, and New Zealand settled, and how did they win self-rule?

As you read this section, complete the chart below to identify the causes and effects of events in the British colonies of Canada, Australia, and New Zealand.

Effect	Ethnic tensions arise between English- and French-speaking Canadians.						
Event	Up to 30,000 loyalists settle in Canada.						
Cause	Loyalist Americans flee to Canada.						

© Pearson Education, Inc., publishing as Pearson Prentice Hall. All rights reserved.

CHAPTER
10
SECTION 3

Section Summary
SELF-RULE FOR CANADA, AUSTRALIA, AND NEW ZEALAND

In Canada, Britain created two provinces: English-speaking Upper Canada and French-speaking Lower Canada. <u>When unrest grew in both colonies, the British sent Lord Durham to compile a report on the causes of the unrest.</u> In response to his report, Parliament joined the two Canadas into one colony in 1840.

As the country grew, Canadian leaders urged **confederation** of Britain's North American colonies. They felt that confederation would strengthen the new nation against the United States' ambitions and help Canada's economic development. Britain finally agreed, and Parliament passed a law that created the Dominion of Canada. As a **dominion,** Canada had its own parliament. As the growing country expanded westward, the way of life of Native Americans was destroyed. People of French and Native American descent, called **métis,** resisted in two revolts. However, government troops put down both uprisings.

In 1770, Captain James Cook claimed Australia for Britain. Like most regions claimed by imperialist powers, Australia had already long been inhabited. The **indigenous** people there are called Aborigines. When white settlers arrived in Australia, the Aborigines suffered. Britain made Australia into a **penal colony** to fill a need for prisons. Then, Britain encouraged free citizens to emigrate to Australia by offering them land and tools. As the newcomers settled in, they thrust aside or killed the Aborigines. Like Canada, Australia was made up of separate colonies scattered around the continent. To counter possible interference from other European powers and to boost development, Britain agreed to Australian demands for self-rule. In 1901, the colonies united into the independent Commonwealth of Australia.

Captain James Cook also claimed New Zealand for Britain. The indigenous people of New Zealand are the **Maori.** The Maori were determined to defend their land. In 1840, Britain annexed New Zealand. As colonists poured in, they took more and more land, leading to fierce wars with the Maori. Many Maori died in the struggle. By the 1870s, resistance crumbled. Like settlers in Australia and Canada, white New Zealanders sought self-rule. In 1907, New Zealand won independence.

Review Questions

1. Why did Britain agree to create the Dominion of Canada?

_____

_____

2. Why did Britain agree to demands for self-rule in Australia?

_____

_____

READING CHECK

What happened to the Aborigines when white settlers arrived in Australia?

_____

_____

_____

VOCABULARY STRATEGY

What does the word *compile* mean in the underlined sentence? Think about research reports you have written for school. What process did you go through to create a report? Use your prior knowledge to help you learn what *compile* means.

READING SKILL

Identify Causes and Effects
Identify the causes and effects of the Maori fight against New Zealand colonists.

_____

_____

_____

© Pearson Education, Inc., publishing as Pearson Prentice Hall. All rights reserved.

CHAPTER 10 SECTION 4

Note Taking Study Guide

ECONOMIC IMPERIALISM IN LATIN AMERICA

Focus Question: How did Latin American nations struggle for stability, and how did industrialized nations affect them?

A. *As you read this section, complete the chart below to identify multiple causes of instability in Latin America. Then, give an example of how each cause affected Mexico.*

Instability in Latin America	
Causes	**Mexican Example**

B. *As you read "The Economics of Dependence" and "The Influence of the United States," complete the chart below to identify effects of foreign influence on Latin America.*

Effects of Foreign Influence		

© Pearson Education, Inc., publishing as Pearson Prentice Hall. All rights reserved.

Section Summary

CHAPTER 10 SECTION 4

ECONOMIC IMPERIALISM IN LATIN AMERICA

Many factors undermined democracy in the newly independent nations of Latin America. Constitutions in these nations guaranteed equality before the law, but inequalities remained. With no tradition of unity, **regionalism** also weakened the new nations. Local strongmen, called *caudillos*, assembled private armies to resist the central government. Power remained in the hands of a privileged few.

Mexico is an example of the challenges faced by many Latin American nations. Large landowners, army leaders, and the Catholic Church dominated Mexican politics. The ruling elite was divided between conservatives and liberals. Conservatives defended the traditional social order. Liberals saw themselves as enlightened supporters of progress. Bitter battles between these two groups led to revolts and the rise of dictators. When **Benito Juárez** and other liberals gained power, they began an era of reform known as **La Reforma.** Juárez offered hope to the oppressed people of Mexico. After Juárez died, however, General Porfirio Díaz ruled as a harsh dictator. Many Indians and mestizos fell into **peonage** to their employers.

Under colonial rule, Latin America was economically dependent on Spain and Portugal, which had prevented the colonies from developing their own economies. After independence, the new Latin American republics did adopt free trade, but Britain and the United States replaced Spain as Latin America's chief trading partners.

As nations like Mexico tried to build stable governments, the United States expanded across North America. To discourage any new European colonization of the Americas, the United States issued the **Monroe Doctrine.** The United States then issued a series of policies claiming "international police power" in the Western Hemisphere. Under these policies, U.S. companies continued to invest in the countries of Latin America. To protect these investments, the United States sent troops to many of these countries, which made the United States a target of increasing resentment and rebellion. When the United States built the **Panama Canal** across Central America, it was an engineering marvel that boosted trade and shipping worldwide. To people in Latin America, however, the canal was another example of "Yankee imperialism."

Review Questions

1. What limited democracy in the independent nations of Latin America?

_____

_____

2. Why did the new Latin American republics remain economically dependent after independence?

_____

_____

READING CHECK

Which Mexican leader offered hope to the oppressed people of Mexico?

_____

_____

_____

VOCABULARY STRATEGY

What does the word *enlightened* mean in the underlined sentence? Break the word into its word parts. Circle the root word, or the word part without the prefix and suffixes. Use the meaning of the root word to help you figure out what *enlightened* means.

READING SKILL

Identify Causes and Effects
Identify what caused the United States to issue the Monroe Doctrine and what its effects were on Latin America.

_____

_____

_____

© Pearson Education, Inc., publishing as Pearson Prentice Hall. All rights reserved.

Focus Question: Why and how did World War I begin in 1914?

As you read this section in your textbook, complete the following chart to summarize the events that led to the outbreak of World War I.

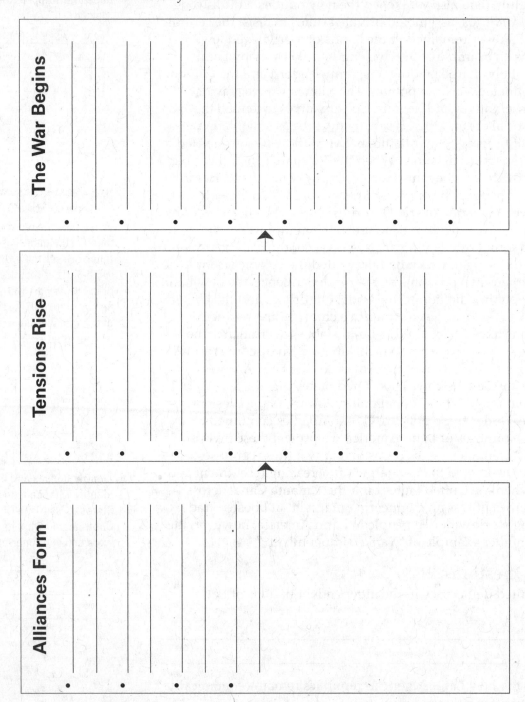

The War Begins

Tensions Rise

Alliances Form

© Pearson Education, Inc., publishing as Pearson Prentice Hall. All rights reserved.

CHAPTER 11 SECTION 1

Section Summary
THE GREAT WAR BEGINS

Although powerful forces were pushing Europe towards war, the great powers had formed alliances signing non-binding agreements, called **ententes,** to try to keep the peace. The Triple Alliance included Germany, Austria-Hungary, and Italy. Russia and France, and later Britain, formed the Triple Entente. During World War I, Germany and Austria fought together as the Central Powers. At that time, Russia, France, and Britain became known as the Allies.

In the decades before 1914, European powers competed to protect their status. Overseas rivalries divided them, as they fought for new colonies in Africa and elsewhere. They began to build up their armies and navies. The rise of **militarism** helped to feed this arms race. At the same time, sensational journalism stirred the public against rival nations.

Nationalism also increased tensions. Germans were proud of their military and economic might. The French yearned for the return of **Alsace and Lorraine.** Russia supported a powerful form of nationalism called Pan-Slavism. This led Russia to support nationalists in Serbia. Austria-Hungary worried that nationalism might lead to rebellions within its empire, while Ottoman Turkey felt threatened by nearby new nations in the Balkans, such as Serbia and Greece. Serbia's dreams of a South Slav state could take land away from both Austria-Hungary and Turkey. Soon, unrest made the Balkans a "powder keg." Then, in 1914, a Serbian nationalist assassinated the heir to the Austrian throne at Sarajevo, Bosnia.

Some Austrian leaders saw this as an opportunity to crush Serbian nationalism. They sent Serbia an **ultimatum,** which Serbia refused to meet completely. Austria, with the full support of Germany, declared war on Serbia in July 1914.

Soon, the network of alliances drew other great powers into the conflict. Russia, in support of Serbia, began to **mobilize** its army. Germany declared war on Russia. France claimed it would honor its treaty with Russia, so Germany declared war on France, too. When the Germans violated Belgian **neutrality** to reach France, Britain declared war on Germany. World War I had begun.

Review Questions

1. How did the network of European alliances cause World War I to develop?

   After Austria declared war, other nations that were allies declared war.

2. What act caused Britain to declare war?

   German invasion of neutral Belgium

READING CHECK

Which countries made up the Central Powers?

Germany
Austria Hungary
Italy

VOCABULARY STRATEGY

What does the word *overseas* mean in the underlined sentence? What clues can you find in the surrounding words, phrases, or sentences? Circle the words in the paragraph that could help you learn what *overseas* means.

READING SKILL

Summarize Describe the events that led Austria to declare war on Serbia.

Gavrilo Princip assassinated Austria's Archduke Franz Ferdinand

© Pearson Education, Inc., publishing as Pearson Prentice Hall. All rights reserved.

Name_____ Class_____ Date_____

Focus Question: How and where was World War I fought?

A. *As you read "Stalemate on the Western Front," "Battle on Other European Fronts," and "War Around the World," complete the following flowchart with important details about each battlefront of World War I.*

Western Front	Eastern Front
• _____	• _____
• _____	• _____
• _____	• _____
• _____	

Elsewhere in Europe	Ottoman Empire
• _____	• _____
• _____	• _____
• _____	**Colonies**
	• _____

B. *As you read "Technology of Modern Warfare," complete the following concept web to summarize information about the technology of World War I. Add ovals as needed.*

© Pearson Education, Inc., publishing as Pearson Prentice Hall. All rights reserved.

Section Summary
A NEW KIND OF WAR

The Great War was the largest conflict in history up to that time. Millions of French, British, Russian, and German soldiers mobilized for battle. German forces fought their way toward France, but Belgian resistance foiled Germany's plans for a quick victory. Both sides dug deep trenches along the battlefront to protect their armies from enemy fire. The fighting on this Western Front turned into a long, deadly **stalemate,** a deadlock that neither side could break.

Technology made World War I different from earlier wars. Modern weapons caused high casualties. In 1915, first Germany then the Allies began using poison gas. Advances in technology brought about the introduction of tanks, airplanes, and modern submarines. Germany used **zeppelins** to bomb the English coast. Both sides equipped airplanes with machine guns. <u>Pilots known as "flying aces" confronted each other in the skies, but these "dog fights" had little effect on the ground war.</u> German submarines, called **U-boats,** did tremendous damage to the Allied shipping. To defend against them, the Allies organized **convoys,** or groups of merchant ships protected by warships.

On Europe's Eastern Front, battle lines shifted back and forth, sometimes over large areas. Casualties rose higher than on the Western Front. Russia was ill-prepared and suffered a disastrous defeat when pushing into eastern Germany. In 1915, Italy declared war on Austria-Hungary and Germany. In 1917, the Austrians and Germans launched a major offensive against the Italians.

Although most of the fighting took place in Europe, World War I was a global conflict. Japan used the war to seize German outposts in China and islands in the Pacific. The Ottoman empire joined the Central Powers. Its strategic location enabled it to cut off Allied supply lines to Russia through the **Dardanelles,** a vital strait.. The Ottoman Turks were hard hit in the Middle East, however. Arab nationalists revolted against Ottoman rule. The British sent **T.E. Lawrence,** or Lawrence of Arabia, to aid the Arabs. European colonies in Africa and Asia were also drawn into the war.

Review Questions

1. Why did a stalemate develop on the Western Front?

   Trech warfare

   _____

2. How did technology make World War I different from earlier wars?

   zeppelins, u-boats, airplanes

   _____

VOCABULARY STRATEGY

What does the word *confronted* mean in the underlined sentence? What clues or examples can you find in the surrounding words that hint at its meaning? Think about what the goal of these pilots was. Circle the words in the underlined sentence that could help you learn what *confronted* means.

READING SKILL

Identify Supporting Details Identify important details that show the differences between the course of the war on the Western Front and on the Eastern Front.

Stalemate or not

progression

east

© Pearson Education, Inc., publishing as Pearson Prentice Hall. All rights reserved.

CHAPTER 11 SECTION 3

Note Taking Study Guide

WINNING THE WAR

Focus Question: How did the Allies win World War I?

As you read this section in your textbook, complete the following outline to summarize the content of this section.

I. **Waging total war**

  A. Economies committed to war production.

    1. Conscription

    2. Rationing

    3. Price controls

  B. Economic warfare

    1. _British navy sets prevents bombing_

    2. _German blockade of U boats_

    3. _Germans sink britian_

  C. _Propoganda_

    1. _press was arts censored_

    2. _Citizens hirected to leave bug or enimy_

    3. _Atrocities exagerated_

  D. _Women join war effort_

    1. _Join workforce_

    2. _Nurses work close to front lines_

    3. _These efforts help to win right to vote_

II. _Morale collapses_

  A. _War fatigue_

    1. _Shortages, heavy casualtys_

    2. _leads to calls for peace_

    3. _troops mutiny or desert_

  B. _Revolution in Russia_

    1. _Bread riots lead to revolution_

    2. _Lennin comes to power_

    3. _Russn withdraws_

(Outline continues on the next page.)

© Pearson Education, Inc., publishing as Pearson Prentice Hall. All rights reserved.

CHAPTER 11 SECTION 3

Note Taking Study Guide

WINNING THE WAR

(Continued from page 94)

III. _____ Why _____ US _____

    A. _____ Why join allies _____

        1. _____ Cultural ties _____

        2. _____ Us _____

        3. _____ Zimmerman note _____

    B. _____ Declaring war _____

        1. _____ 1917 Wilson asks congress to declare war _____

        2. _____ 1918, US troops _____ western front _____

        3. _____ war _____

    C. _____ 14 points _____

        1. _____ Resolve future wars _____

        2. _____ self determination _____

        3. _____ Assertion of _____

IV. _____ Victory _____ nations _____

    A. _____ 1918 filled _____ battle on western front _____

    B. _____ Kaiser flees _____

    C. _____ Government seeks armistice _____

© Pearson Education, Inc., publishing as Pearson Prentice Hall. All rights reserved.

CHAPTER 11 SECTION 3 — Note Taking Study Guide
WINNING THE WAR

READING CHECK

Why did women take on new jobs during the war?

As men left job
to fight, women
took over to keep
economys up

VOCABULARY STRATEGY

What does the word *eroded* mean in the underlined sentence? What clues or examples can you find in the surrounding words, phrases, or sentences that hint at its meaning? Circle the words in the paragraph that could help you learn what *eroded* means.

READING SKILL

Summarize Describe what made World War I a total war.

devoted all
resources to the
war.

World War I was a **total war,** in which the participants channeled all their resources into the war effort. Both sides set up systems to recruit, arm, transport, and supply their armies. Nations imposed universal military **conscription,** or "the draft," requiring all young men to be ready to fight. Women also played a critical role. As millions of men left to fight, women took over their jobs and kept national economies going.

International law allowed wartime blockades to confiscate **contraband,** but British blockades kept ships from carrying other supplies, such as food, in and out of Germany. In retaliation, German U-boats torpedoed the British passenger liner *Lusitania.* Both sides used **propaganda** to control public opinion, circulating tales of **atrocities,** some true and others completely made up.

As time passed, war fatigue set in. Long casualty lists, food shortages, and the failure to win led to calls for peace. The morale of both troops and civilians plunged. In Russia, stories of incompetent generals and corruption eroded public confidence and led to revolution.

Until 1917, the United States had been neutral, but in that year it declared war on Germany. Many factors contributed to this decision, including Germany's unrestricted submarine warfare. Also, many Americans supported the Allies because of cultural ties with Britain and sympathy for its fellow democracy, France. By 1918, about two million fresh American soldiers had joined the war-weary Allied troops on the Western Front. In that year, President Wilson also issued his **Fourteen Points,** his terms for resolving this and future wars. Among the most important was **self-determination** for peoples in Eastern Europe.

A final showdown on the Western Front began in March 1918. With American troops, the Allies drove back German forces. In September, German generals told the kaiser that the war could not be won. The kaiser stepped down and the new German government sought an **armistice** with the Allies. At 11 A.M. on November 11, 1918, the Great War at last came to an end.

Review Questions

1. What caused the morale of troops and civilians to plunge?

war fatigue, food shortage, lay casualty
lists, failure to win.

2. What are two factors that caused the United States to enter the war?

submarine.

cultural ties

© Pearson Education, Inc., publishing as Pearson Prentice Hall. All rights reserved.

Note Taking Study Guide
MAKING THE PEACE

Focus Question: What factors influenced the peace treaties that ended World War I, and how did people react to the treaties?

A. *As you read "The Costs of War," complete this concept web to summarize the costs of World War I.*

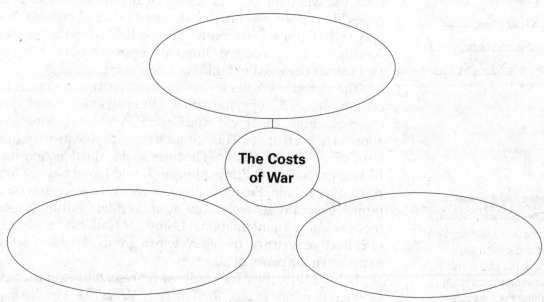

B. *As you read "The Paris Peace Conference," "The Treaty of Versailles," and "Outcome of the Peace Settlements," complete this table to categorize issues and problems that resulted from agreements made after the war.*

Issue	Treaty Settlement	Problems
War Debt		
Fear of German Strength		
Nationalism		
Colonies and Other Non-European Territories		
League of Nations		

© Pearson Education, Inc., publishing as Pearson Prentice Hall. All rights reserved.

CHAPTER 11 SECTION 4

Section Summary

MAKING THE PEACE

READING CHECK

Which three main Allied leaders negotiated the terms of the Treaty of Versailles?

British David Loyd
French Georges Clemenceau
U.S. Pres Wilson

VOCABULARY STRATEGY

What does the word *widespread* mean in the underlined sentence? Look at the two words that form this compound word, and think about their meanings. Use what you know about the parts of this compound word to figure out its meaning.

READING SKILL

Summarize How did the goals of the three main leaders at the Paris Peace Conference differ?

Wanted to rebuild
Britain, punish
France, establish
League of Nations

The human, material, and political costs of World War I were staggering. The huge loss of life was made even worse in 1918 by a deadly **pandemic** of influenza. From France to Russia, homes, farms, factories, and roads had been bombed into rubble. Reconstruction costs and war debts would burden an already battered world. The Allies blamed the war on their defeated foes and insisted that they make **reparations.** Governments had collapsed in Russia, Germany, Austria-Hungary, and the Ottoman empire. Out of the chaos, political **radicals** dreamed of building a new social order.

The victorious Allies met at the Paris Peace Conference to discuss the fate of Europe, the former Ottoman empire, and various colonies around the world. The Central Powers and Russia were not allowed to participate. This would lead to problems regarding the issue of self-determination. The three main Allied leaders had conflicting goals. British Prime Minister David Lloyd George focused on rebuilding Britain. French leader Georges Clemenceau wanted to punish Germany severely. American President Wilson insisted on the creation of an international League of Nations, based on the idea of **collective security.** In this system, a group of nations acts as one to preserve the peace of all.

In June 1919, the Allies ordered representatives of the new German Republic to sign the Treaty of Versailles. The German delegates were horrified. The treaty forced Germany to assume full blame for the war. The treaty also imposed huge reparations that would burden an already damaged German economy and limited the size of Germany's military.

The Allies drew up treaties with the other Central Powers. <u>Like the Treaty of Versailles, these treaties left widespread dissatisfaction, especially among many colonies that had hoped for an end to imperial rule.</u> Many nations felt betrayed by the peacemakers. As a result of these treaties, new nations emerged where the German, Austrian, and Russian empires had once ruled. Outside Europe, the Allies added to their overseas empires. The treaties also created a system of **mandates.** The one ray of hope was the establishment of the League of Nations. The failure of the United States to support the League, however, weakened the League's power.

Review Questions

1. What were some of the human, material, and political costs of the war?

Homes, farms, factories, roads,
pandemic

2. Why were German representatives at Versailles horrified?

Because they had to assume full
blame for the war

© Pearson Education, Inc., publishing as Pearson Prentice Hall. All rights reserved.

CHAPTER 11 SECTION 5
Note Taking Study Guide
REVOLUTION AND CIVIL WAR IN RUSSIA

Focus Question: How did two revolutions and a civil war bring about Communist control of Russia?

As you read the section, fill in the following timeline with dates and facts about the series of events that led to Communist control of Russia. Then write two sentences summarizing the information in the timeline.

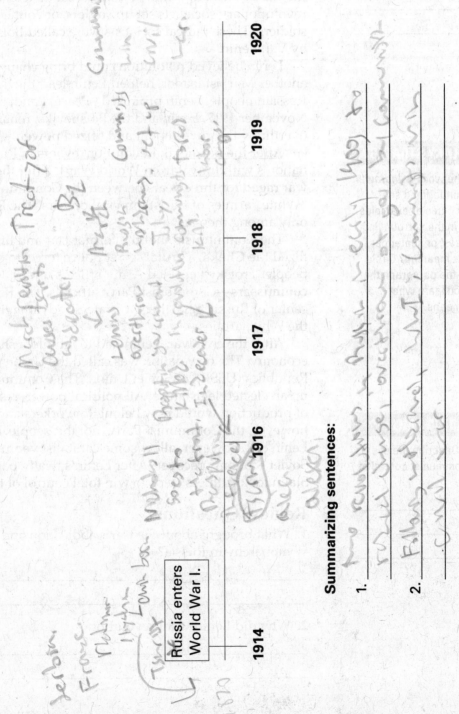

Russia enters World War I.

Summarizing sentences:

1. _____

2. _____

© Pearson Education, Inc., publishing as Pearson Prentice Hall. All rights reserved.

Name_____ Class_____ Date_____

READING CHECK

What was the name of the new Communist nation?

USSR

Soviet uwon.

_____

VOCABULARY STRATEGY

What does the word *withdrawal* mean in the underlined sentence? What clues or examples can you find in the surrounding words, phrases, or sentences that hint at its meaning? Circle the words in the paragraph that could help you learn what *withdrawal* means.

READING SKILL

Summarize Describe the events that led to Communist control of Russia.

collaps of monarchy

revolution

_____

At the beginning of the 1900s, Russia had many political, economic, and social problems. Tsar Nicholas II resisted change. Marxists tried to ignite revolution among the **proletariat.** World War I quickly strained Russian resources. By March 1917, disasters on the battlefield and shortages at home brought the monarchy to collapse, and the tsar abdicated. While politicians set up a temporary government, revolutionary socialists set up **soviets,** or councils of workers and soldiers. These radical socialists were called Bolsheviks and were led by V. I. Lenin.

Lenin believed revolution could bring change. Leon Trotsky, another Marxist leader, helped Lenin lead the fight. To the weary Russian people, Lenin promised "Peace, Land, and Bread." In November 1917, Lenin and the Bolsheviks, renamed Communists, overthrew the government and seized power.

After the Bolshevik Revolution, events in Russia led to the nation's withdrawal from World War I. After the withdrawal, civil war raged for three years between the Communist "Reds" and the "White" armies of tsarist imperial officers. The Russians now fought only among themselves.

The Communists shot the former tsar and his family. They organized the **Cheka,** a brutal secret police force, to control their own people. Trotsky kept Red Army officers under the close watch of **commissars**—Communist Party officials. The Reds' position in the center of Russia gave them a strategic advantage, and they defeated the White armies.

After the civil war, Lenin had to rebuild a shattered state and economy. The new nation was called the Union of Soviet Socialist Republics (USSR), or Soviet Union. The Communist constitution set up an elected legislature. All political power, resources, and means of production would now belong to workers and peasants. In reality, however, the Communist Party, not the people, had all the power. Lenin did, however, allow some capitalist ventures that helped the Soviet economy recover. After Lenin's death, party leader Joseph Stalin took ruthless steps to win total control of the nation.

Review Questions

1. What brought about the tsar's abdication and the end of the monarchy in Russia?

   Disasters on battlefield and shortage at home.

2. Why did Lenin want revolution?

   So that it could bring change

_____

© Pearson Education, Inc., publishing as Pearson Prentice Hall. All rights reserved.

CHAPTER 12 SECTION 1 — Note Taking Study Guide
STRUGGLE IN LATIN AMERICA

Focus Question: How did Latin Americans struggle for change in the early 1900s?

A. *As you read the "The Mexican Revolution" and "Revolution Leads to Change," complete the chart by listing the causes and effects of the Mexican Revolution.*

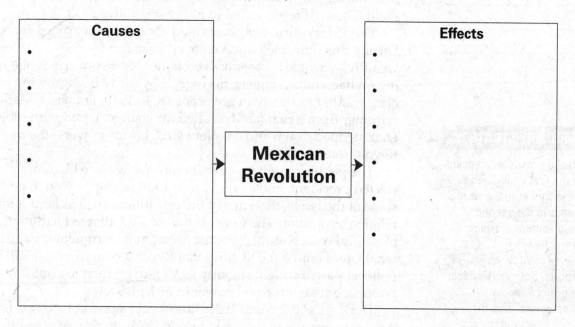

Causes

•
•
•
•
•

→ Mexican Revolution →

Effects

•
•
•
•
•
•

B. *As you read "Nationalism at Work in Latin America," complete the following chart as you list the effects of nationalism in Latin America.*

Effects of Nationalism in Latin America

Economic	Political	Cultural
•	•	•
•	•	•
•		•

© Pearson Education, Inc., publishing as Pearson Prentice Hall. All rights reserved.

CHAPTER 12
SECTION 1

Section Summary
STRUGGLE IN LATIN AMERICA

READING CHECK

What was the PRI, and what was its impact on Mexico?

_____

_____

_____

In the early 1900s, exports kept Latin America's economy booming. Even though foreign investors controlled much of the natural resources, stable governments helped keep economies strong. Yet turmoil brewed because military leaders and wealthy landowners held most of the power. Workers and peasants had no say in government. These differences led to increasing unrest.

Dictator Porfirio Díaz had ruled Mexico for nearly 35 years. During this time, the nation enjoyed peace and success, but only the wealthy benefited. Peasants lived in desperate poverty while working on **haciendas,** large farms owned by the rich. A growing middle class wanted more say in government. In 1910, Francisco Madero, a reformer from a rich family, called for change. Faced with rebellion, Díaz stepped down and a violent struggle for power—the Mexican Revolution—began.

The people fought for years before Venustiano Carranza was elected president, and a new constitution was approved. It addressed some of the issues that caused the revolution, such as land reform, religion, and labor. The Constitution of 1917 allowed **nationalization** of natural resources. In 1929, the Mexican government organized what later became the Institutional Revolutionary Party (PRI). This political party brought stability to Mexico by carrying out some reforms, but kept the real power in its hands.

VOCABULARY STRATEGY

What does the word *intervening* mean in the first underlined sentence? It is similar to the word *interference* in the second underlined sentence. You may have heard the word *interference* used when you watch sports. Both words begin with the prefix *inter-*, which means "between." Use the meaning of *inter-* and the context clues to help you figure out what *intervening* means.

During the 1920s and 1930s, the Great Depression caused Latin American exports to drop and import prices to rise. As a result, **economic nationalism** became popular. Latin Americans wanted to develop their own industries. Some Latin American nations took over foreign-owned companies. The government became more powerful when people accepted authoritarian leaders, hoping that they could improve the economy. Along with economic nationalism, there was a growth in **cultural nationalism.** Artists such as Diego Rivera painted murals or large images of Mexico's history, culture, and the people's struggles. The United States also became more involved in Latin America, often intervening to protect U.S. interests or troops. This led to anti-American feelings. Under the **Good Neighbor Policy,** the United States promised less interference in Latin American affairs.

READING SKILL

Identify Causes and Effects
What were two effects of United States involvement in Latin America?

_____

_____

_____

Review Questions

1. Under Porfirio Díaz, which groups had the most power?

_____

_____

2. How did the Great Depression lead to economic nationalism?

_____

_____

© Pearson Education, Inc., publishing as Pearson Prentice Hall. All rights reserved.

Note Taking Study Guide
NATIONALISM IN AFRICA AND THE MIDDLE EAST

Focus Question: How did nationalism contribute to changes in Africa and the Middle East following World War I?

As you read this section in your textbook, complete the following table to identify the causes and effects of the rise of nationalism.

Rise of Nationalism

Region	Reasons for Rise	Effects
Africa	• • • •	• • •
Turkey and Persia	• • •	• • • •
Middle East	• • • •	• •

© Pearson Education, Inc., publishing as Pearson Prentice Hall. All rights reserved.

CHAPTER 12 SECTION 2 — Section Summary
NATIONALISM IN AFRICA AND THE MIDDLE EAST

Europe ruled over most of Africa during the early 1900s. Improved farming methods meant more exports; however, this mostly benefited colonial rulers. Europeans kept the best lands, and African farmers were forced to grow cash crops instead of food. They also were forced to work in mines and then pay taxes to the colonial governments. Many Africans began criticizing imperial rule, but their freedoms only eroded further. An example was the system of **apartheid** in South Africa. Under this policy, black Africans were denied many of their previous rights, such as the right to vote.

During the 1920s, the **Pan-Africanism** movement called for the unity of Africans and people of African descent around the world. During the first Pan-African Congress, delegates asked world leaders at the Paris Peace Conference to approve a charter of rights for Africans. Their request was ignored. The members of the **négritude movement** in West Africa and the Caribbean protested colonial rule while expressing pride in African culture. These movements, however, brought about little real change.

In **Asia Minor,** Mustafa Kemal overthrew the Ottoman ruler and established the republic of Turkey. Also referred to as Atatürk (father of the Turks), his government promoted industrial expansion by building factories and railroads. Inspired by Atatürk's successes, Reza Khan overthrew the shah of Persia. Khan sought to turn Persia into a modern country. He, too, built factories and railroads. Khan also demanded a bigger portion of profits for Persia from British-controlled oil companies. Both leaders pushed aside Islamic traditions, replacing them with Western alternatives.

VOCABULARY STRATEGY

What does the word *advocated* mean in the underlined sentence? What clues can you find in the surrounding sentences? Think about why Britain issued the Balfour Declaration. Use this information to help you understand the meaning of *advocated*.

Pan-Arabism was a movement based on a shared history of Arabs living from the Arabian Peninsula to North Africa. Leaders of Arab nations and territories had hoped to gain independence after World War I, but felt betrayed when France and Britain were given control over their lands. In Palestine, Arab nationalists faced Zionists, or Jewish nationalists. To win the support of European Jews, Britain issued the **Balfour Declaration.** In it, the British advocated for a "national home for the Jewish people" in Palestine. Arabs felt the declaration favored the Jews. As a result, an ongoing conflict developed in the Middle East.

READING SKILL

Identify Causes and Effects
What was one effect of the Balfour Declaration?

_____

_____

Review Questions

1. How did colonial rule hurt Africans?

_____

_____

2. How did Reza Khan change Persia?

_____

_____

© Pearson Education, Inc., publishing as Pearson Prentice Hall. All rights reserved.

CHAPTER

12

SECTION 3

Note Taking Study Guide

INDIA SEEKS SELF-RULE

Focus Question: How did Gandhi and the Congress party work for independence in India?

As you read this section in your textbook, complete the following chart by recording the causes and effects of Gandhi's leadership on India's independence movement.

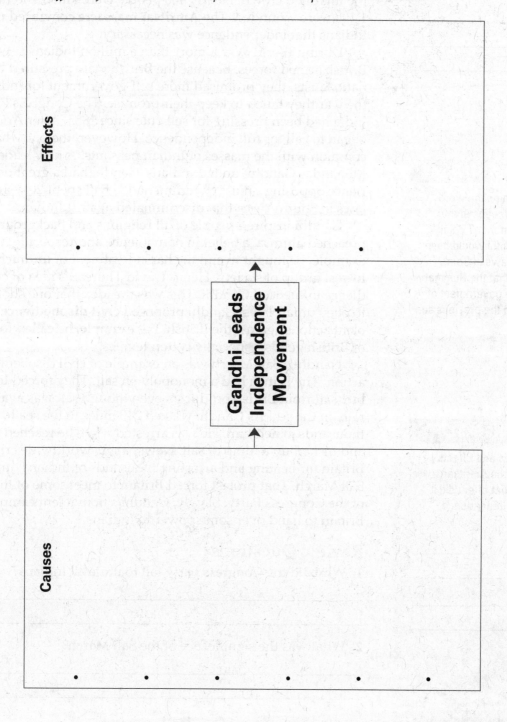

© Pearson Education, Inc., publishing as Pearson Prentice Hall. All rights reserved.

CHAPTER 12 SECTION 3

Section Summary

INDIA SEEKS SELF-RULE

READING CHECK

What had Gandhi done before becoming a leader for Indian independence?

_____

_____

_____

VOCABULARY STRATEGY

What do you think the word *discriminated* means in the underlined sentence? Think about why Gandhi would have been fighting laws in South Africa. Note what the Summary says about the government of South Africa in the previous sentence.

READING SKILL

Identify Causes and Effects What caused the Amritsar massacre? What effect did it have on the independence movement?

Cause:_____

_____

Effect:_____

_____

In 1919, Indian protests against colonial rule led to riots and attacks on British residents. The British then banned public meetings. On April 13, 1919, a peaceful crowd of Indians gathered in an enclosed field in Amritsar. As Indian leaders spoke, British soldiers fired on the unarmed crowd. Nearly 400 people were killed and more than 1,100 were wounded. The **Amritsar massacre** convinced many Indians that independence was necessary.

During World War I, more than a million Indians served in the British armed forces. Because the British were pressured by Indian nationalists, they promised more self-government for India. After the war they failed to keep their promise. The Congress Party of India had been pressing for self-rule since 1885. After Amritsar it began to call for full independence. However, the party had little in common with the masses of Indian peasants. A new leader, Mohandas Gandhi, united Indians. Gandhi had a great deal of experience opposing unjust government. He had spent 20 years fighting laws in South Africa that discriminated against Indians.

Gandhi inspired people of all religions and backgrounds. He preached **ahimsa,** a belief in nonviolence and respect for all life. For example, he fought to end the harsh treatment of **untouchables,** the lowest group of society. Henry David Thoreau's idea of civil disobedience influenced Gandhi. This was the idea that one should refuse to obey unfair laws. Gandhi proposed **civil disobedience** and nonviolent actions against the British. For example, he called for a **boycott** of British goods, especially cotton textiles.

Gandhi's Salt March was an example of civil disobedience in action. The British had a monopoly on salt. They forced Indians to buy salt from British producers even though salt was available naturally in the sea. As Gandhi walked 240 miles to the sea to collect salt, thousands joined him. He was arrested when he reached the water and picked up a lump of salt. Newspapers worldwide criticized Britain for beating and arresting thousands of Indians during the Salt March. That protest forced Britain to meet some of the demands of the Congress Party. Slowly, Gandhi's nonviolent campaign forced Britain to hand over some power to Indians.

Review Questions

1. Why did the Congress party fail to unite all Indians?

_____

_____

2. What was the significance of the Salt March?

_____

_____

© Pearson Education, Inc., publishing as Pearson Prentice Hall. All rights reserved.

CHAPTER
12
SECTION 4

Note Taking Study Guide
UPHEAVALS IN CHINA

Focus Question: How did China cope with internal division and foreign invasion in the early 1900s?

A. *As you read "The Chinese Republic in Trouble," complete the following chart by listing the multiple causes of upheaval in the Chinese Republic.*

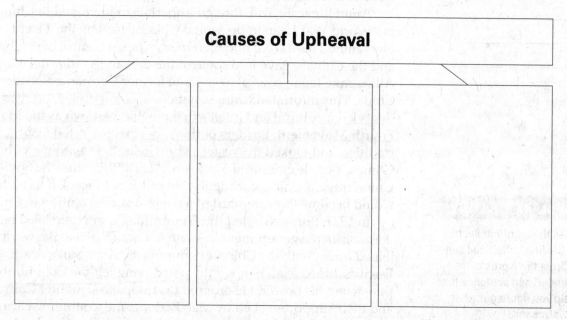

Causes of Upheaval

B. *As you read "Struggle for a New China" and "Japanese Invasion," complete the chart to sequence the fighting among the Guomindang, the warlords, the Chinese Communists, and the Japanese.*

1926
- Guomindang and Communists defeat warlords.

© Pearson Education, Inc., publishing as Pearson Prentice Hall. All rights reserved.

CHAPTER 12 SECTION 4

Section Summary

UPHEAVALS IN CHINA

READING CHECK

What group of people spearheaded the May Fourth Movement?

_____

_____

_____

VOCABULARY STRATEGY

What does the word *intellectual* mean in the first underlined sentence? Circle the words in the second underlined sentence that could help you figure out what *intellectual* means.

READING SKILL

Recognize Multiple Causes
Why did Chinese peasants support the Communists?

_____

_____

_____

When the Qing dynasty collapsed in 1911, Sun Yixian became president of China's new republic. He hoped to rebuild China, but he made little progress. The country fell into chaos when local warlords seized power and the economy fell apart. Millions of peasants suffered severe hardships. Sun Yixian stepped down as president in 1912.

Amid the upheaval, foreign imperialism increased in China. During World War I, Japan presented Chinese leaders the **Twenty-One Demands.** These were intended to give Japan control over China, and the Chinese gave into some of the demands. After the war, the Allies gave Japan control over some former German possessions in China. This infuriated Chinese nationalists. As protests spread, students led a cultural and intellectual rebellion known as the **May Fourth Movement.** Leaders of this movement rejected Confucian tradition and looked to Western knowledge and learning. Other Chinese people embraced Marxism. Also at this time, the Soviet Union trained Chinese students and military officers, hoping they would become the **vanguard** of a communist revolution in China.

In 1921, Sun Yixian led the **Guomindang,** or Nationalist party, as it established a government in south China. To defeat the warlords he joined forces with the Chinese communists. After Sun's death, Jiang Jieshi assumed leadership of the party. Jiang felt the Communists threatened his power. He ordered his troops to slaughter Communists and their supporters. Led by Mao Zedong, the Communist army escaped north in what became known as the **Long March.** During the March, Mao's soldiers fought back using guerrilla tactics. Along the way, Mao's soldiers treated the peasants kindly. They paid for the goods they needed and were careful not to destroy crops. Many peasants had suffered because of the Guomindang, so they supported the Communists.

While Jiang pursued the Communists across China, the Japanese invaded Manchuria, adding it to their growing empire. Then, in 1937, Japanese planes bombed Chinese cities and Japanese soldiers marched into Nanjing, killing hundreds of thousands of people. In response, Jiang and Mao formed an alliance to fight the invaders. The alliance held up until the end of the war with Japan.

Review Questions

1. How did Japan gain territory and control of areas of China during World War I?

_____

_____

2. Why did Jiang and Mao form an alliance?

_____

_____

© Pearson Education, Inc., publishing as Pearson Prentice Hall. All rights reserved.

CHAPTER 12 SECTION 5 — Note Taking Study Guide
CONFLICTING FORCES IN JAPAN

Focus Question: How did Japan change in the 1920s and 1930s?

As you read this section in your textbook, complete the table by listing the effects of liberalism and militarism in Japan during the 1920s and 1930s.

Conflicting Forces in Japan	
Liberalism in the 1920s	**Militarism in the 1930s**
•	•
•	•
•	•
•	•

© Pearson Education, Inc., publishing as Pearson Prentice Hall. All rights reserved.

CHAPTER 12 SECTION 5

Section Summary
CONFLICTING FORCES IN JAPAN

READING CHECK

Who became emperor of Japan in 1926?

_____

_____

_____

VOCABULARY STRATEGY

What does the word *manipulated* mean in the underlined sentence? Think about the Latin root *manus*, which means "hand" or "to handle." How did the zaibatsu "handle" politicians? Use this information about the word's root to help you understand what *manipulated* means.

READING SKILL

Understand Effects What effect did the Great Depression have on Japanese politics?

_____

_____

_____

The Japanese economy grew during World War I, based on the export of goods to the Allies and increased production. At this time, Japan also expanded its influence throughout East Asia and sought further rights in China. Additionally, Japan gained control of some former German possessions in China after the war. **Hirohito** became emperor of Japan in 1926, and during his reign, the country experienced both success and tragedy

In the 1920s, the Japanese government moved toward greater democracy. All adult men gained the right to vote, regardless of social class. Despite greater democratic freedoms, however, the zaibatsu, a group of powerful business leaders, manipulated politicians. By donating to political parties, the zaibatsu were able to push for policies that favored their interests.

Peasants and factory workers did not share in the nation's prosperity. Young Japanese rejected tradition and family authority. There was tension between the government and the military. The Great Depression fed the discontent of the military and the extreme nationalists, or **ultranationalists.** They resented Western limits on the expansion of Japan's empire. As the economic crisis worsened, the ultranationalists set their sights on **Manchuria** in northern China. In 1931, a group of Japanese army officers set explosives to blow up railroad tracks in Manchuria. They blamed it on the Chinese and used it as an excuse to invade. Without consulting government leaders, the military conquered Manchuria. Politicians objected to the army's actions, but the people sided with the military. When the League of Nations condemned the invasion, Japan withdrew from the organization.

Militarists and ultranationalists increased their power in the 1930s. Extremists killed some politicians and business leaders who opposed expansion. To please the ultranationalists, the government suppressed most democratic freedoms. Japan planned to take advantage of China's civil war and conquer the country. In 1939, however, World War II broke out in Europe. The fighting quickly spread to Asia. Earlier, Japan had formed an alliance with Germany and Italy. In September 1940, Japan's leaders signed the Tripartite Pact linking the three nations. Together, the three nations formed the Axis Powers.

Review Questions

1. Describe the economic success of Japan in the 1920s.

_____

_____

2. How did militarists and ultranationalists increase their power in the 1930s?

_____

_____

© Pearson Education, Inc., publishing as Pearson Prentice Hall. All rights reserved.

CHAPTER
13
SECTION 1

Note Taking Study Guide
POSTWAR SOCIAL CHANGES

Focus Question: What changes did Western society and culture experience after World War I?

As you read this section in your textbook, complete the concept web below to identify supporting details related to "Changes to Society" and "Cultural Changes."

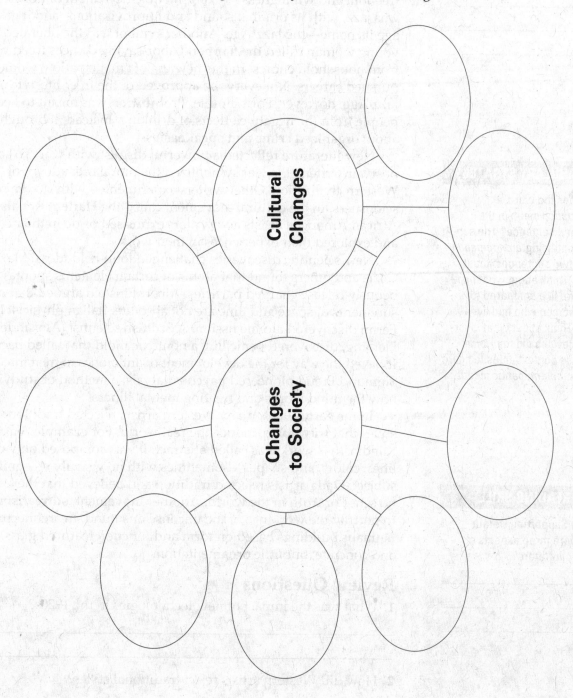

© Pearson Education, Inc., publishing as Pearson Prentice Hall. All rights reserved.

CHAPTER 13 SECTION 1

Section Summary

POSTWAR SOCIAL CHANGES

READING CHECK

What were two symbols of American culture in the 1920s?

_____

_____

_____

VOCABULARY STRATEGY

What does the word *emancipation* mean in the underlined sentence? The sentence containing *emancipation* follows two sentences about women. Think about what flappers were like compared to young women who had lived before. Think about what labor-saving devices did for women. Use these context clues to figure out what *emancipation* means.

READING SKILL

Identify Supporting Details
What were three aspects of postwar literature?

_____

_____

_____

In reaction to World War I, society and culture in the United States and elsewhere underwent rapid changes. During the 1920s, new technologies helped create a mass culture, and to connect people around the world. American culture was characterized by a greater freedom and willingness to experiment. One symbol of this new age was jazz, with its original sound and improvisations, and it gave the age its name—the Jazz Age. Another symbol was the liberated young woman called the **flapper.** Labor-saving devices freed women from household chores. In this new era of emancipation, women pursued careers. Not everyone approved of the freer lifestyle of the Jazz Age, however. For example, **Prohibition** was meant to keep people from the negative effects of drinking. Instead, it brought about organized crime and **speakeasies.**

New literature reflected a powerful disgust with war. To some postwar writers, the war symbolized the moral breakdown of Western civilization. Other writers experimented with stream of consciousness. In the cultural movement called the **Harlem Renaissance,** African American artists and writers expressed pride in their culture and explored their experiences in their work.

New scientific discoveries challenged long-held ideas. Marie Curie and others found that atoms of certain elements spontaneously release charged particles. Albert Einstein argued that measurements of space and time are not absolute. Italian physicist Enrico Fermi discovered atomic fission. A Scottish scientist, Alexander Fleming, discovered penicillin, a nontoxic mold that killed bacteria. It paved the way for the development of antibiotics to treat infections. Sigmund Freud pioneered **psychoanalysis,** a method of studying how the mind works and treating mental illness.

In the early 1900s, many Western artists rejected traditional styles that tried to reproduce the real world. For example, Vasily Kandinsky's work was called **abstract.** It was composed only of lines, colors, and shapes—sometimes with no visually recognizable subject. **Dada** artists rejected tradition and believed that there was no sense or truth in the world. Another movement, **surrealism,** tried to portray the workings of the unconscious mind. In architecture, Bauhaus buildings based on form and function featured glass, steel, and concrete, but little ornamentation.

Review Questions

1. What was the impact of new technologies in the 1920s?

_____

_____

2. How did Western artists reject traditional styles?

_____

_____

© Pearson Education, Inc., publishing as Pearson Prentice Hall. All rights reserved.

Note Taking Study Guide

THE WESTERN DEMOCRACIES STUMBLE

Focus Question: What political and economic challenges did the leading democracies face in the 1920s and 1930s?

A. *As you read "Politics in the Postwar World," Postwar Foreign Policy," and "Postwar Economics," complete the chart below to identify the main ideas under each heading.*

Postwar Issues			
Country	**Politics**	**Foreign Policy**	**Economics**

B. *As you read "The Great Depression," and "The Democracies React to the Depression," complete the chart below to identify the main ideas on the causes, effects, and reactions related to the Great Depression.*

The Great Depression

Causes
-
-
-
-
-

Effects
-
-
-

Reactions
-
-
-

© Pearson Education, Inc., publishing as Pearson Prentice Hall. All rights reserved.

CHAPTER 13 SECTION 2

Section Summary

THE WESTERN DEMOCRACIES STUMBLE

How did Britain and France pay back their war loans to the United States?

_____

_____

_____

VOCABULARY STRATEGY

What does the word *affluent* mean in the underlined sentence? *Affluent* comes from a Latin word that means "to flow." Ask yourself what people have a lot of if they are *affluent*. Use these clues to help you figure out the meaning of *affluent*.

READING SKILL

Identify Main Ideas Write a sentence that summarizes the main idea of this Summary.

_____

_____

_____

In 1919, after World War I, Britain, France, and the United States appeared powerful. However, postwar Europe faced grave problems. The most pressing issues were finding jobs for veterans and rebuilding war-ravaged lands. These problems made radical ideas more popular. Britain had to deal with growing socialism and the "Irish question." Fear of radicals set off a "Red Scare" in the United States.

The three democracies also faced international issues. Concern about a strong Germany led France to build the **Maginot Line** and insist on strict enforcement of the Versailles treaty. Many nations signed the **Kellogg-Briand Pact** promising to "renounce war as an instrument of national policy." In this optimistic spirit, the great powers pursued **disarmament.** Unfortunately, neither the Kellogg-Briand Pact nor the League of Nations had the power to stop aggression. Ambitious dictators in Europe noted this weakness.

The war affected economies all over the world. Both Britain and France owed huge war debts to the United States and relied on reparation payments from Germany to pay their loans. Britain was deeply in debt, with high unemployment and low wages. In 1926, a **general strike** lasted nine days and involved three million workers. On the other hand, the French economy recovered fairly quickly, and the United States emerged as the world's top economic power. In the affluent 1920s, middle-class Americans enjoyed the benefits of capitalism, buying cars, radios, and refrigerators.

However, better technologies allowed factories to make more products faster, leading to **overproduction** in the United States. Factories then cut back, and many workers lost their jobs. A crisis in **finance** led the **Federal Reserve** to raise interest rates. This made people even more nervous about the economy. In the autumn of 1929, financial panic set in. Stock prices crashed. The United States economy entered the **Great Depression,** which soon spread around the world.

Governments searched for solutions. In the United States, President **Franklin D. Roosevelt** introduced the programs of the **New Deal.** Although the New Deal failed to end the Depression, it did ease much suffering. However, as the Depression wore on, it created fertile ground for extremists.

Review Questions

1. After the war, what international agreement was intended to ensure peace?

_____

_____

2. What economic problems did Britain face after the war?

_____

_____

© Pearson Education, Inc., publishing as Pearson Prentice Hall. All rights reserved.

Note Taking Study Guide

FASCISM IN ITALY

Focus Question: How and why did fascism rise in Italy?

A. *As you read "Mussolini's Rise to Power" and Mussolini's Rule," complete the flowchart below as you identify the main ideas under each heading.*

Dissatisfaction and Unrest	Mussolini Takes Power	Mussolini Changes Italy
•	•	•
•	•	•
•	•	•
	•	

B. *As you read "The Nature of Fascism," use the table below to identify the main ideas for each heading.*

What Is Fascism?	
Values	
Characteristics	
Differences from Communism	
Similarities to Communism	

© Pearson Education, Inc., publishing as Pearson Prentice Hall. All rights reserved.

CHAPTER 13 SECTION 3

Section Summary

FASCISM IN ITALY

VOCABULARY STRATEGY

What does the word *proclaimed* mean in the underlined sentence? Think about the function of a poster. How does the purpose of a poster help explain the meaning of *proclaimed*?

READING SKILL

Identify Main Ideas How did Mussolini's Fascists take over Italy?

_____

_____

_____

After World War I, Italian nationalists were outraged when Italy received just some of the territories promised by the Allies. Chaos ensued as peasants seized land, workers went on strike, veterans faced unemployment, trade declined, and taxes rose. The government could not end the crisis. Into this turmoil stepped **Benito Mussolini,** the organizer of the Fascist party. Mussolini's supporters, the **Black Shirts,** rejected democratic methods and favored violence for solving problems. In the 1922 **March on Rome,** tens of thousands of Fascists swarmed the capital. Fearing civil war, the king asked Mussolini to form a government as prime minister.

Mussolini soon suppressed rival parties, muzzled the press, rigged elections, and replaced elected officials with Fascists. Critics were thrown into prison, forced into exile, or murdered. Secret police and propaganda bolstered the regime. In 1929, Mussolini also received support from the pope. Mussolini brought the economy under state control, but basically preserved capitalism. His system favored the upper class and industry leaders. Workers were not allowed to strike, and their wages were kept low. In Mussolini's new system, loyalty to the state replaced conflicting individual goals. "Believe! Obey! Fight!" loudspeakers blared and posters proclaimed. Fascist youth groups marched in parades chanting slogans.

Mussolini built the first modern **totalitarian state.** In this form of government, a one-party dictatorship attempts to control every aspect of the lives of its citizens. Today, we usually use the term **fascism** to describe the underlying ideology of any centralized, authoritarian governmental system that is not communist. Fascism is rooted in extreme nationalism. Fascists believe in action, violence, discipline, and blind loyalty to the state. They praise warfare. They are anti-democratic, rejecting equality and liberty. Fascists oppose communists on important issues. Communists favor international action and the creation of a classless society. Fascists are nationalists who support a society with defined classes. Both base their power on blind devotion to a leader or the state. Both flourish during economic hard times.

Fascism appealed to Italians because it restored national pride, provided stability, and ended the political feuding that had paralyzed democracy in Italy.

Review Questions

1. What was the result of the March on Rome?

_____

_____

2. How are communism and fascism similar?

_____

_____

© Pearson Education, Inc., publishing as Pearson Prentice Hall. All rights reserved.

Note Taking Study Guide
THE SOVIET UNION UNDER STALIN

Focus Question: How did Stalin transform the Soviet Union into a totalitarian state?

As you read this section in your textbook, complete the chart below by identifying the main ideas about the Soviet Union under Stalin for each heading.

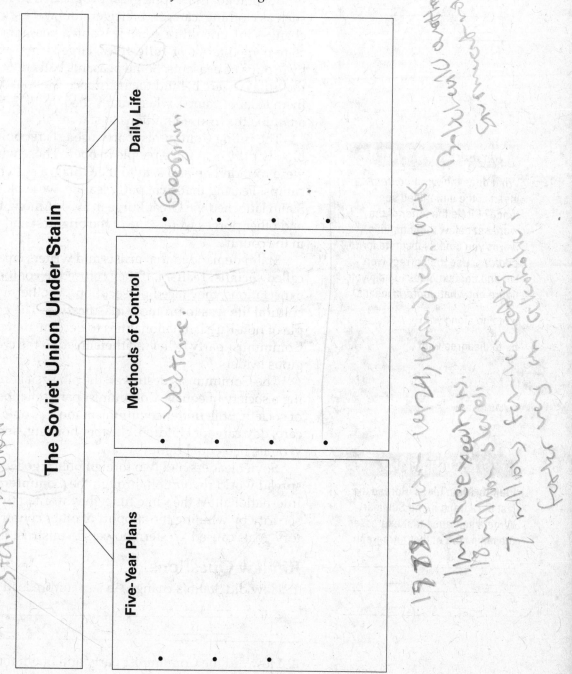

The Soviet Union Under Stalin

Daily Life
- Googshn.
- •
- •
- •

Methods of Control
- Xdtcme.
- •
- •
- •

Five-Year Plans
- •
- •
- •

© Pearson Education, Inc., publishing as Pearson Prentice Hall. All rights reserved.

CHAPTER 13 SECTION 4
Section Summary
THE SOVIET UNION UNDER STALIN

What is a command economy?

The state makes
all the economic
decisions

What does the word *conform* mean in the underlined sentence? Circle the letter of the word set below that contains words you could substitute for *to conform*. Use the correct word set and context clues to help you figure out what *conform* means.

a. to go along with

b. to disagree with

Identify Main Ideas Reread the last paragraph in the Summary. Write a sentence that expresses the main idea of that paragraph.

Soviet Union
wanted to
impose Comintern
& national security

Under Joseph Stalin, the Soviet Union grew into a totalitarian state, controlling all aspects of life, including agriculture, culture, art, and religion. The state also developed a **command economy,** in which it made all economic decisions. Stalin's five-year plans set high production goals. Despite great progress in some sectors, products such as clothing, cars, and refrigerators were scarce. Stalin forced changes in agriculture, too. He wanted peasants to farm on either state-owned farms or **collectives,** large farms owned and operated by groups of peasants. Some peasants balked. Stalin believed that the **kulaks** were behind the resistance. He took their land and sent them to labor camps, where many died. In 1932, Stalin's policies led to a famine that caused millions to starve.

The ruling Communist party used secret police, torture, and bloody purges to force people to obey. Those who opposed Stalin were rounded up and sent to the **Gulag,** a system of brutal labor camps. Fearing that rival party leaders were plotting against him, Stalin launched the Great Purge in 1934. Among the victims of this and other purges were some of the brightest and most talented people in the country.

Stalin demanded that artists and writers create works in a style called **socialist realism.** <u>If they refused to conform to government expectations, they faced persecution.</u> Another way Stalin controlled cultural life was to promote **russification.** The goal was to force people of non-Russian nationalities to become more Russian. The official Communist party belief in **atheism** led to the cruel treatment of religious leaders.

The Communists destroyed the old social order. Instead of creating a society of equals, Communist party members became the heads of society. Still, under communism most people enjoyed free medical care, day care for children, cheaper housing, and public recreation. Women had equal rights by law.

Soviet leaders had two foreign policy goals. They hoped to spread world revolution through the **Comintern,** or Communist International. At the same time, they wanted to ensure their nation's security by winning the support of other countries. These contradictory goals caused Western powers to mistrust the Soviet Union.

Review Questions

1. How did Stalin's changes in agriculture lead to a famine?

He wanted peasants to farm
on state-owned or collectives

2. How did the Communist party and Stalin force people to obey?

Used secret police, torture, and
purges to strike fear

© Pearson Education, Inc., publishing as Pearson Prentice Hall. All rights reserved.

CHAPTER 13 SECTION 5

Note Taking Study Guide

HITLER AND THE RISE OF NAZI GERMANY

Focus Question: How did Hitler and the Nazi Party establish and maintain a totalitarian government in Germany?

As you read this section in your textbook, complete the flowchart below to identify the main ideas about Hitler and the rise of Nazi Germany for each heading.

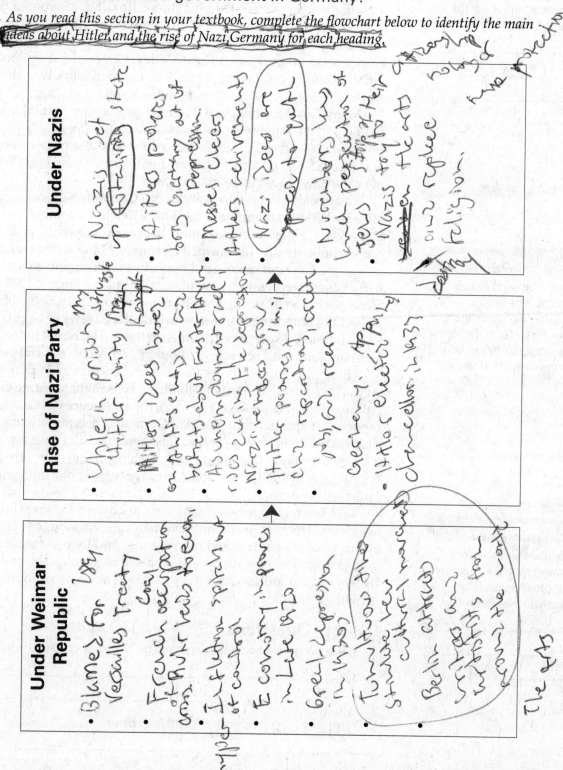

Under Weimar Republic
- Blamed for 1939 Versailles Treaty
- French occupation of Ruhr leads to econ.
- hyper-inflation spirals out of control
- Economy improves in late 1920s
- Great Depression in 1929
- Turmoil and standard low culture/marches
- Berlin attracts artists and novelists from around the world

The arts

Rise of Nazi Party
- While in prison struggle Hitler writes Mein Kampf
- As Hitler sees bigger in Nazi's electoral car beliefs about foster Aryan
- As unemployment rose during the depression Nazi's members grow
- Hitler promises to end reparations, occur, employ, reach
- electorate. AP party
- Hitler elected party chancellor in 1933

Under Nazis
- Nazis set up Totalitarian state
- Hitler's party bans Germany out of depression
- Messes elect Hitler's achievements
- Nazi ideas are forced to gradl.
- Nuremberg laws permission of Jews strip of their rights, Nazis try to replace their hearts religion.

CHAPTER 13 SECTION 5

Section Summary

HITLER AND THE RISE OF NAZI GERMANY

READING CHECK

What was the purpose of the Nuremberg Laws?

_____

_____

_____

After World War I, German leaders set up a democratic government known as the Weimar Republic. The Weimar constitution established a parliamentary system led by a **chancellor.** It gave women the right to vote and included a bill of rights. However, the new republic faced severe problems. When Germany could not make its war reparations France seized the coal-rich **Ruhr Valley.** Government actions led to inflation and skyrocketing prices. The German mark was almost worthless. Many middle-class families lost their savings.

Many Germans believed that energetic leader Adolf Hitler would solve Germany's problems. As head of the Nazi party, Hitler promised to end reparations, create jobs, and rearm Germany. He was elected chancellor in 1933, and within a year he was dictator over the new fascist state in Germany.

To appeal to nationalism and recall Germany's glorious past, Hitler called his government the **Third Reich.** To combat the Depression, Hitler launched public works programs. In violation of the Versailles treaty, he rearmed Germany. Hitler relied on his secret police, the **Gestapo,** to root out opposition. He organized a brutal system of terror, repression, and totalitarian rule. A fanatical anti-Semite, Hitler set out to drive the Jews from Germany. In 1935, the Nazis passed the **Nuremberg Laws,** which deprived Jews of German citizenship and placed severe restrictions on them. The Nazis indoctrinated German youth and rewrote textbooks to reflect Nazi racial views.

VOCABULARY STRATEGY

What does the word *regime* mean in the underlined sentence? Circle the words in the sentence that refer to the phrase "the new *regime.*" What do you think is the meaning of *regime?*

Hitler also limited women's roles and encouraged "pure-blooded Aryan" women to bear many children. He sought to purge German culture of what he believed were corrupt influences. Nazis denounced modern art and jazz, but glorified German artists and myths. Hitler despised Christianity as "weak." He combined all Protestant sects into a single state church. Although many clergy either supported the new regime or remained silent, some courageously spoke out against Hitler's government.

Like Germany, most new nations in Eastern Europe slid from systems of democratic to authoritarian rule. Economic problems and ethnic tensions contributed to instability and helped fascist rulers to gain power. The new dictators promised to keep order, and won the backing of the military and the wealthy. They also supported the growth of anti-Semitism.

READING SKILL

Identify Main Ideas Reread the last paragraph in the Summary. Write the main idea of that paragraph on the lines below.

_____

_____

_____

Review Questions

1. What were the basic features of the Weimar constitution?

_____

_____

2. Why did many Germans support Hitler?

_____

_____

© Pearson Education, Inc., publishing as Pearson Prentice Hall. All rights reserved.

CHAPTER 14 SECTION 1

Note Taking Study Guide
FROM APPEASEMENT TO WAR

Focus Question: What events unfolded between Chamberlain's declaration of "peace in our time" and the outbreak of a world war?

A. *As you read "Aggression Goes Unchecked" and "Spain Collapses into Civil War," complete the chart below to record the sequence of events that led to the outbreak of World War II.*

Acts of Aggression	
Japan	• _____
	• _____
Italy	• _____
Germany	• _____
	• _____
Spain	• _____

B. *As you read "German Aggression Continues" and "Europe Plunges Toward War," complete the timetable below to recognize the sequence of German aggression.*

German Aggression	
March 1938	
September 1938	
March 1939	
September 1939	

© Pearson Education, Inc., publishing as Pearson Prentice Hall. All rights reserved.

Name_____ Class_____ Date_____

Who were the members of the Axis powers?

_____

_____

_____

What does the word *sanctions* mean in the underlined sentence? Look at the words, phrases, and sentences surrounding the word. Use the context clues you find to help you figure out the meaning of *sanctions*.

Recognize Sequence What happened in Spain before Francisco Franco started a civil war there?

_____

_____

_____

Throughout the 1930s, dictators took aggressive action. Yet, they met only verbal protests and pleas for peace from Western powers. For example, when the League of Nations condemned Japan's invasion of Manchuria in 1931, Japan simply withdrew from the League. A few years later, Japanese armies invaded China, starting the Second Sino-Japanese War. Meanwhile, Mussolini invaded Ethiopia in 1935. The League of Nations voted sanctions against Italy, but the League had no power to enforce its punishment of Mussolini. Hitler, too, defied the Western democracies by building up the German military and sending troops into the "demilitarized" Rhineland. This went against the Treaty of Versailles. The Western democracies denounced Hitler but adopted a policy of **appeasement.** Appeasement developed for a number of reasons, including widespread **pacifism.** The United States responded with a series of **Neutrality Acts.** The goal was to avoid involvement in a war, rather than to prevent one. While the Western democracies sought to avoid war, Germany, Italy, and Japan formed an alliance. It became known as the **Axis powers.**

In Spain, a new, more liberal government passed reforms that upset conservatives. General **Francisco Franco,** who was opposed to the new government, started a civil war. Hitler and Mussolini supported Franco, their fellow fascist. The Soviet Union sent troops to support the anti-Fascists, or Loyalists. The governments of Britain, France, and the United States remained neutral, although individuals from these countries fought with the Loyalists. By 1939, Franco had triumphed.

German aggression continued. In 1938, Hitler forced the **Anschluss,** or union with Austria. Next, Hitler set his sights on the **Sudentenland.** This was a part of Czechoslovakia where three million Germans lived. At the Munich Conference, which was held to discuss the situation, British and French leaders chose appeasement and allowed Hitler to annex the territory.

In March 1939, Hitler took over the rest of Czechoslovakia. Months later, Hitler and Stalin signed the **Nazi-Soviet Pact.** They agreed not to fight if the other went to war. This paved the way for Germany's invasion of Poland in September of 1939, which set off World War II.

Review Questions

1. How did the United States respond to the aggressive action of dictators in the 1930s?

_____

_____

2. What was the result of the Munich Conference?

_____

_____

© Pearson Education, Inc., publishing as Pearson Prentice Hall. All rights reserved.

Name_____ Class_____ Date_____

CHAPTER 14
SECTION 2

Note Taking Study Guide
THE AXIS ADVANCES

Focus Question: Which regions were attacked and occupied by the Axis powers, and what was life like under their occupation?

A. *As you read "The Axis Attacks," "Germany Invades the Soviet Union," and "Japan Attacks the United States," use the chart below to record the sequence of events.*

September 1939: Germany invades Poland.

B. *As you read "Life Under Nazi and Japanese Occupation," use the concept web to identify supporting details about the occupations.*

Nazi occupation

Japanese occupation

© Pearson Education, Inc., publishing as Pearson Prentice Hall. All rights reserved.

CHAPTER 14 SECTION 2

Section Summary
THE AXIS ADVANCES

READING CHECK

What was the name of the German government in southern France?

_____

_____

_____

VOCABULARY STRATEGY

Find the word *nullified* in the underlined sentence. In math class you might have learned that there is nothing, or zero, in the null set. Use this clue about related words to help you figure out the meaning of *nullified*.

READING SKILL

Sequence Events When did the United States declare neutrality?

_____

_____

_____

In September 1939, Nazi forces launched a **blitzkrieg** against Poland. First the **Luftwaffe,** the German air force, bombed. Then, tanks and troops pushed their way in. At the same time, Stalin invaded from the east, grabbing land. Within a month, Poland ceased to exist.

Then, in early 1940, Hitler conquered Norway, Denmark, the Netherlands, and Belgium. By May, German forces had bypassed France's Maginot Line. British forces that had been sent to help the French were trapped. In a desperate scheme, the British rescued their troops from **Dunkirk.** However, in June, the French were forced to surrender. Germany occupied northern France and set up a puppet state, the **Vichy** government, in the south.

The British, led by Winston Churchill, remained defiant against Hitler. In response, Hitler launched bombing raids over British cities that lasted from September 1940 until June 1941. Despite this blitz, Hitler was not able to take Britain. Meanwhile, Hitler sent one of his best commanders, **General Erwin Rommel,** to North Africa. Rommel had a string of successes there. In the Balkans, German and Italian forces added Greece and Yugoslavia to the growing Axis territory. At the same time, the Japanese were occupying lands in Asia and the Pacific.

In June 1941, Hitler nullified the Nazi-Soviet Pact by invading the Soviet Union. Stalin was unprepared, and the Soviet army suffered great losses. The Germans advanced toward Moscow and Leningrad. During a lengthy siege of Leningrad, more than a million Russians died. The severe Russian winter finally slowed the German army.

As they marched across Europe, the Nazis sent millions to **concentration camps** to work as slave laborers. Even worse, Hitler established death camps to kill those he judged racially inferior. Among many others, some six million Jews were killed in what became known as the **Holocaust.**

The United States declared neutrality at the beginning of the war. Yet many Americans sympathized with those who fought the Axis powers. Congress passed the **Lend-Lease Act** of 1941, allowing the United States to sell or lend war goods to foes of the Axis. On December 7, 1941, the Japanese bombed the U.S. fleet at Pearl Harbor. Four days later, Congress declared war on Japan.

Review Questions

1. What countries were conquered by Germany in 1939 and 1940?

_____

_____

2. What was the purpose of the Lend-Lease Act?

_____

_____

© Pearson Education, Inc., publishing as Pearson Prentice Hall. All rights reserved.

CHAPTER 14 SECTION 3
Note Taking Study Guide
THE ALLIES TURN THE TIDE

Focus Question: How did the Allies begin to push back the Axis powers?

As you read this section in your textbook, complete the chart below to record the sequence of events that turned the tide of the war in favor of the Allies.

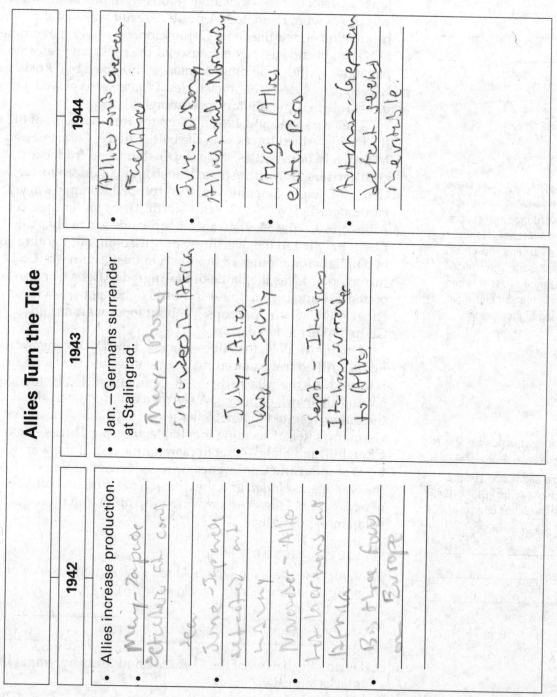

Allies Turn the Tide

1944
- Allies and German fighting
- June - D-Day Allies invade Normandy
- Aug. Allies enter Paris
- Autumn - German defeat seems inevitable

1943
- Jan.—Germans surrender at Stalingrad.
- May - North surrendered Africa
- July - Allies land in Sicily
- Sept - Italy Italy surrender to Allies

1942
- Allies increase production.
- May - To pue schedule at cord sea
- June - Japanese defeated at Midway
- November - Allies let Germans at Africa
- Battle for free Europe

© Pearson Education, Inc., publishing as Pearson Prentice Hall. All rights reserved.

CHAPTER 14 SECTION 3	Section Summary
	THE ALLIES TURN THE TIDE

READING CHECK

Who were the "Big Three"?

_____

_____

_____

VOCABULARY STRATEGY

Find the word *incessant* in the underlined sentence. Notice that the phrase "around-the-clock" follows *incessant*. They have similar meanings. Use this context clue to help you figure out the meaning of *incessant*.

READING SKILL

Recognize Sequence List the sequence of events in 1942–1943 that gave the Allies control of North Africa.

_____

_____

_____

To defeat the Axis powers in World War II, the Allies devoted all their resources to the war effort. Governments took a greater role in the economy. For example, governments ordered factories to make tanks instead of cars. Consumer goods were rationed, and wages and prices were regulated. A positive result was that the increase in production ended the Great Depression. However, governments also limited citizens' rights, censored the press, and resorted to propaganda. At the same time, women, symbolized by **"Rosie the Riveter,"** replaced men in factories. Women also played a more direct role in some military operations.

The years 1942 and 1943 marked the turning point of the war. In the Pacific, Allied forces won the battles of the Coral Sea and Midway. In both battles, attacks were launched from enormous **aircraft carriers.** In North Africa, British and American forces, led by General **Dwight Eisenhower,** soon trapped Rommel's army, and he surrendered in May 1943. With North Africa under their control, the Allies crossed the Mediterranean and landed in Sicily. Allied victories in Italy led to the overthrow of Mussolini, but fighting continued in Italy for another 18 months. On the Eastern front, a key turning point was the Battle of **Stalingrad.** After a German advance on the city and brutal house-to-house fighting, the Soviet army encircled the German troops. Without food or ammunition, the Germans surrendered.

On June 6, 1944, the Allies launched the **D-Day** invasion of France. Allied troops faced many obstacles, but the Germans finally retreated. <u>As the Allies advanced, Germany reeled from incessant, around-the-clock bombing.</u> A German counterattack, the Battle of the Bulge, resulted in terrible losses on both sides. However, with Germany's defeat seeming inevitable, the "Big Three"—Roosevelt, Churchill, and Stalin—met to plan for the end of the war. Key features of this **Yalta Conference** were the Soviet agreement to enter the war against Japan and the division of Germany into four zones of occupation. However, growing mistrust at Yalta foreshadowed a split among the Allies.

Review Questions

1. Name three ways in which Allied governments took a greater role in the economy during World War II.

_____

_____

2. During the battles of the Coral Sea and Midway, from where were attacks launched?

_____

_____

© Pearson Education, Inc., publishing as Pearson Prentice Hall. All rights reserved.

Note Taking Study Guide

VICTORY IN EUROPE AND THE PACIFIC

Focus Question: How did the Allies finally defeat the Axis powers?

As you read this section in your textbook, complete the timeline below to sequence the events that led to the defeat of the Axis powers.

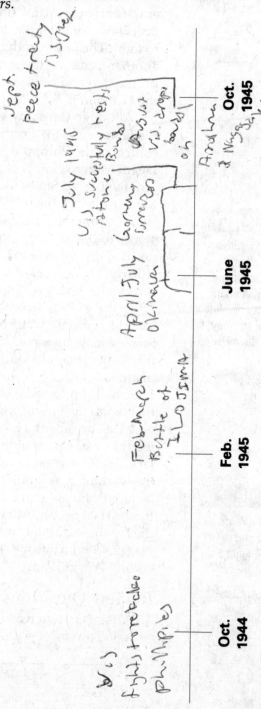

Sept.
Peace treaty signed

July 1945
U.S. successfully tests atomic bomb

Germany surrenders

August
U.S. drops atomic bomb

Hiroshima & Nagasaki

April July
Okinawa

February
Battle of Iwo Jima

U.S.
fights to retake
Philippines

Oct. 1945

June 1945

Feb. 1945

Oct. 1944

© Pearson Education, Inc., publishing as Pearson Prentice Hall. All rights reserved.

CHAPTER 14 SECTION 4

Section Summary

VICTORY IN EUROPE AND THE PACIFIC

READING CHECK

What was the "island-hopping" campaign?

_____

_____

_____

VOCABULARY STRATEGY

What does the word *objective* mean in the underlined sentence? Say the sentence aloud and omit *objective*. Think about other words that might complete the sentence. Use this strategy to help you figure out the meaning of *objective*.

READING SKILL

Recognize Sequence Create a timeline of the events that took place in Japan from August 6 to August 10, 1945.

_____

_____

_____

In Europe, World War II officially ended on May 8, 1945, or **V-E Day.** The Allies were able to defeat the Axis powers for many reasons. Because of their location, the Axis powers had to fight on several fronts at the same time. Hitler also made some poor military decisions. For example, he underestimated the Soviet Union's ability to fight. The huge productive capacity of the United States was another factor. At the same time, Allied bombing hindered German production and caused oil to become scarce. This nearly grounded the Luftwaffe.

Although Germany was defeated, the Allies still had to defeat the Japanese in the Pacific. By May 1942, the Japanese had gained control of the Philippines, killing thousands during the **Bataan Death March.** However, after the battles of Midway and the Coral Sea, the United States took the offensive. General **Douglas MacArthur** began an **"island-hopping"** campaign to recapture islands from the Japanese. The captured islands served as stepping-stones to the next objective—Japan. The Americans gradually moved north and were able to blockade Japan. Bombers pounded Japanese cities and industries. At the same time, the British pushed Japanese forces back into the jungles of Burma and Malaya.

In early 1945, bloody battles on Iwo Jima and Okinawa showed that the Japanese would fight to the death rather than surrender. Some young Japanese became **kamikaze** pilots who flew their planes purposefully into U.S. ships. While Allied military leaders planned to invade, scientists offered another way to end the war. They had conducted research, code-named the **Manhattan Project,** that led to the building of an atomic bomb for the United States. The new U.S. president, Harry Truman, decided that dropping the bomb would save American lives. The Allies first issued a warning to the Japanese to surrender or face "utter and complete destruction," but the warning was ignored. On August 6, 1945, a U.S. plane dropped an atomic bomb on the city of **Hiroshima,** instantly killing more than 70,000 people. Many more died from radiation sickness. When the Japanese did not surrender, another bomb was dropped on **Nagasaki** on August 9. The next day, Japan finally surrendered, ending World War II.

Review Questions

1. What were two reasons why the Allies were able to defeat the Axis powers?

_____

_____

2. Why did Truman decide to drop the atomic bomb on Japan?

_____

_____

© Pearson Education, Inc., publishing as Pearson Prentice Hall. All rights reserved.

CHAPTER
14
SECTION 5

Note Taking Study Guide
THE END OF WORLD WAR II

Focus Question: What issues arose in the aftermath of World War II and how did new tensions develop?

As you read this section in your textbook, sequence the events following World War II by completing the outline below.

I. The War's Aftermath

   A. Devastation

      1. As many as 50 million are dead.

      2. _____

   B. _____

      1. _____

      2. _____

      3. _____

   C. _____

      1. _____

      2. _____

II. _____

   A. _____

      1. _____

   B. _____

      1. _____

      2. _____

   C. _____

      1. _____

      2. _____

III. _____

   A. _____

      1. _____

      2. _____

   B. _____

      1. _____

      2. _____

(Outline continues on the next page.)

© Pearson Education, Inc., publishing as Pearson Prentice Hall. All rights reserved.

CHAPTER 14 SECTION 5

Note Taking Study Guide

THE END OF WORLD WAR II

(Continued from page 129)

3. _____

IV. _____

  A. _____

    1. _____

    2. _____

    3. _____

  B. _____

    1. _____

    2. _____

    3. _____

  C. _____

    1. _____

    2. _____

    3. _____

    4. _____

  D. _____

    1. _____

    2. _____

    3. _____

  E. _____

    1. _____

    2. _____

  F. _____

    1. _____

    2. _____

© Pearson Education, Inc., publishing as Pearson Prentice Hall. All rights reserved.

CHAPTER 14 SECTION 5

Section Summary

THE END OF WORLD WAR II

While the Allies enjoyed their victory, the huge costs of World War II began to emerge. As many as 50 million people had been killed. The Allies also learned the full extent of the horrors of the Holocaust. War crimes trials, such as those at **Nuremberg** in Germany, held leaders accountable for their wartime actions. To ensure tolerance and peace, the Western Allies set up democratic governments in Japan and Germany.

In 1945, delegates from 50 nations convened to form the **United Nations.** Under the UN Charter, each member nation has one vote in the General Assembly. A smaller Security Council has greater power. It has five permanent members: the United States, the Soviet Union (today Russia), Britain, France, and China. Each has the right to veto any council decision. UN agencies have tackled many world problems, from disease to helping refugees.

However, conflicting ideologies soon led to a **Cold War.** This refers to the state of tension and hostility between the United States and the Soviet Union from 1946 to 1990. Soviet leader Stalin wanted to spread communism into Eastern Europe. He also wanted to create a buffer zone of friendly countries as a defense against Germany. By 1948, pro-Soviet communist governments were in place throughout Eastern Europe.

When Stalin began to threaten Greece and Turkey, the United States outlined a policy called the **Truman Doctrine.** This policy meant that the United States would resist the spread of communism throughout the world. To strengthen democracies in Europe, the United States offered a massive aid package, called the **Marshall Plan.** Western attempts to rebuild Germany triggered a crisis over the city of Berlin. The Soviets controlled East Germany, which surrounded Berlin. To force the Western Allies out of Berlin, the Soviets blockaded West Berlin, but a yearlong airlift forced them to end the blockade.

However, tensions continued to mount. In 1949, the United States and nine other nations formed a new military alliance called the **North Atlantic Treaty Organization (NATO).** The Soviets responded by forming the **Warsaw Pact,** which included the Soviet Union and seven Eastern European nations.

Review Questions

1. What was the purpose of the post-World War II war crimes trials?

_____

_____

2. Why did the United States offer aid under the Marshall Plan to European countries?

_____

_____

READING CHECK

What was the Cold War?

_____

_____

_____

VOCABULARY STRATEGY

What does the word *convened* mean in the underlined sentence? The word *convene* comes from the Latin *convenire.* In Latin, *con-* means "together" and *venire* means "to come." Use this word-origins clue to help you figure out the meaning of *convened.*

READING SKILL

Recognize Sequence List the sequence of events that led to the Berlin airlift.

_____

_____

_____

© Pearson Education, Inc., publishing as Pearson Prentice Hall. All rights reserved.

Note Taking Study Guide

CHAPTER 15 SECTION 1

THE COLD WAR UNFOLDS

Focus Question: What were the military and political consequences of the Cold War in the Soviet Union, Europe, and the United States?

As you read this section in your textbook, complete the following chart to summarize the consequences of the Cold War in the Soviet Union, Europe, and the United States.

Consequences of the Cold War

Soviet Union
-
-
-
-
-
-
-

Europe
-
-
-
-
-

United States
-
-
-
-
-
-
-
-
-

© Pearson Education, Inc., publishing as Pearson Prentice Hall. All rights reserved.

Section Summary

THE COLD WAR UNFOLDS

After World War II, the United States and the Soviet Union emerged as **superpowers.** They each created military alliances made up of nations they protected or occupied. <u>The United States helped form the North Atlantic Treaty Organization (NATO), which comprised Western European allies.</u> The Soviet Union signed the Warsaw Pact with Eastern European countries. The line between the democratic West and communist East was called the Iron Curtain. Many revolts challenging Soviet domination were extinguished with military force.

The superpowers also engaged in a weapons race—both developed nuclear weapons. To reduce the threat of war, the two sides held several disarmament talks. One agreement was intended to limit the use of **anti-ballistic missiles (ABMs).** These weapons were designed to shoot down missiles launched by hostile nations. The ABMs were considered a threat because they could give one side more protection, which might encourage it to attack. Then during the 1980s, President **Ronald Reagan** proposed a missile defense program called "Star Wars." Other agreements limited the number of nuclear weapons that nations could maintain, which eased Cold War tensions. This period was called the era of **détente.** It ended, however, when the Soviet Union invaded Afghanistan in 1979.

During the 1950s, **Fidel Castro** led a revolution in Cuba and became its leader. To bring down Castro's communist regime, U.S. President **John F. Kennedy** supported an invasion of Cuba, but the attempt failed. One year later, the Soviets sent nuclear missiles to Cuba. Many feared a nuclear war. After the United States blockaded Cuba, Soviet leader **Nikita Khrushchev** agreed to remove the missiles.

The Soviets wanted to spread communist **ideology** around the globe. When Khrushchev came to power, he eased censorship and increased tolerance. However, repression returned under **Leonid Brezhnev.** American leaders followed a policy of **containment.** This was a strategy of keeping communism from spreading to other nations. In addition, a "red scare" in the United States resulted in Senator Joseph McCarthy leading an internal hunt for communists in the government and military. The House Un-American Activities Committee (HUAC) also sought out communist sympathizers.

Review Questions

1. What did the two superpowers do to reduce the threat of war during the Cold War?

_____

_____

2. What ended the period of détente between the United States and the Soviet Union?

_____

_____

READING CHECK

Who were the two superpowers during the Cold War?

_____

_____

_____

VOCABULARY STRATEGY

What does the word *comprised* mean in the underlined sentence? What clues can you find in the surrounding words, phrases, or sentences? Use these context clues to help you figure out what *comprised* means.

READING SKILL

Summarize What was the United States policy known as containment?

_____

_____

_____

© Pearson Education, Inc., publishing as Pearson Prentice Hall. All rights reserved.

CHAPTER 15 SECTION 2

Note Taking Study Guide
THE INDUSTRIALIZED DEMOCRACIES

Focus Question: How did the United States, Western Europe, and Japan achieve economic prosperity and strengthen democracy during the Cold War years?

As you read this section in your textbook, use the chart below to categorize economic and political changes in the industrialized democracies.

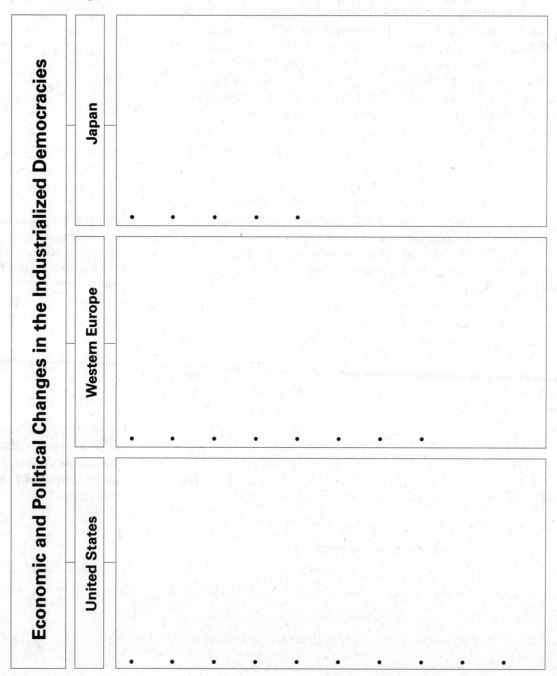

Economic and Political Changes in the Industrialized Democracies

Japan

- • • • •

Western Europe

- • • • • • • •

United States

- • • • • • • • • • • •

© Pearson Education, Inc., publishing as Pearson Prentice Hall. All rights reserved.

Section Summary

CHAPTER 15 SECTION 2

THE INDUSTRIALIZED DEMOCRACIES

During the postwar period, U.S. businesses expanded into the global marketplace. Other nations needed goods and services to rebuild. This led to a period of economic success that changed life in the United States. During the 1950s and 1960s, **recessions** were brief and mild. <u>As Americans prospered, they left the cities to live in the suburbs.</u> This trend is called **suburbanization.** Also, job opportunities in the Sunbelt attracted many people to that region. By the 1970s, however, a political crisis in the Middle East made Americans aware of their dependence on imported oil. The price of oil and gas rose substantially, which meant that people had less money to buy other products. The decades of prosperity ended in 1974 with a serious recession.

During the period of prosperity, African Americans and other minorities faced **segregation** in housing and education. They suffered from **discrimination** in jobs and voting. **Dr. Martin Luther King, Jr.,** emerged as the main civil rights leader in the 1960s. The U.S. Congress passed some civil rights legislation. Other minority groups were inspired by the movement's successes. For example, the women's rights movement helped to end much gender-based discrimination.

Western Europe rebuilt after World War II. The Marshall Plan helped restore European economies by providing U.S. aid. After the war, Germany was divided between the communist East and the democratic West, but reunited at the end of the Cold War in 1990. Under **Konrad Adenauer,** West Germany's chancellor from 1949 to 1963, Germany built modern cities and re-established trade. European governments also developed programs that increased government responsibility for the needs of people. These **welfare states** required high taxes to pay for their programs. During the 1980s, some leaders, such as Britain's Margaret Thatcher, reduced the role of the government in the economy. Western Europe also moved closer to economic unity with the **European Community**, an organization dedicated to establishing free trade among its members.

Japan also prospered after World War II. Its **gross domestic product (GDP)** soared. Like Germany, Japan built factories. The government protected industries by raising tariffs on imported goods. This helped create a trade surplus for Japan.

Review Questions

1. What caused a U.S. recession in 1974?

_____

_____

2. Explain how Germany rebuilt its economy after World War II.

_____

_____

READING CHECK

What is suburbanization?

_____

_____

_____

VOCABULARY STRATEGY

What does the word *prospered* mean in the underlined sentence? The word *decline* is an antonym of *prosper.* It means to "sink," "descend," or "deteriorate." Use these meanings of *decline* to figure out the meaning of *prospered.*

READING SKILL

Categorize In what ways were minorities denied equality and opportunity?

_____

_____

© Pearson Education, Inc., publishing as Pearson Prentice Hall. All rights reserved.

Name_____ Class_____ Date_____

Focus Question: What did the Communist victory mean for China and the rest of East Asia?

As you read this section in your textbook, complete the flowchart below to help you summarize the effects of the Communist Revolution on China and the impact of the Cold War on China and Korea.

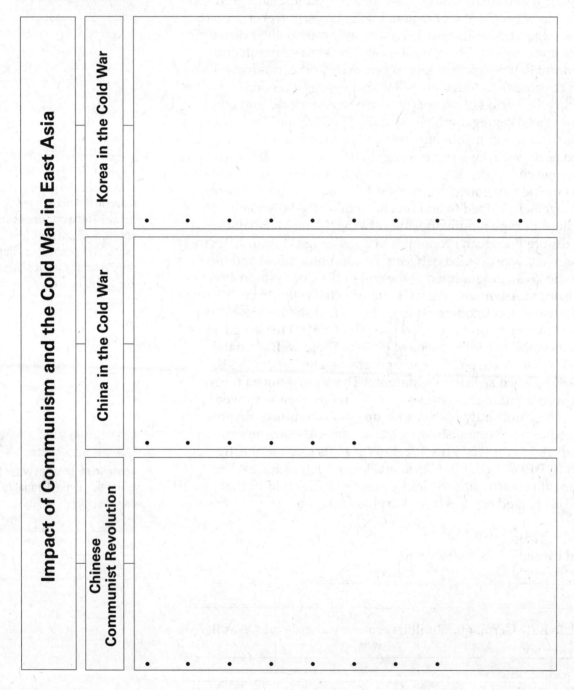

Impact of Communism and the Cold War in East Asia

Korea in the Cold War

China in the Cold War

Chinese Communist Revolution

© Pearson Education, Inc., publishing as Pearson Prentice Hall. All rights reserved.

CHAPTER 15 SECTION 3

Section Summary

COMMUNISM SPREADS IN EAST ASIA

After World War II, Mao Zedong led communist forces to victory over Jiang Jieshi's Nationalists, who fled to Taiwan. Then Mao began to reshape China's economy. First, he gave land to peasants, but then called for **collectivization.** Under this system, <u>Mao moved people from their small villages and individual farms into communes of thousands of people on thousands of acres.</u> Known as the **Great Leap Forward,** the program was intended to increase farm and industrial production. Instead, it produced low quality, useless goods and less food. Bad weather also affected crops, and many people starved.

To remove "bourgeois" tendencies from China, Mao began the **Cultural Revolution.** Skilled workers and managers were removed from factories and forced to work on farms or in labor camps. This resulted in a slowed economy and a threat of civil war.

At first, the United States supported the Nationalist government in Taiwan. The West was concerned that the Soviet Union and China would become allies, but border clashes led the Soviets to withdraw aid and advisors from China. U.S. leaders thought that by "playing the China card," or improving relations with the Chinese, they would further isolate the Soviets. In 1979, the United States established diplomatic relations with China.

Korea was an independent nation until Japan invaded it in World War II. After the war, American and Soviet forces agreed to divide the Korean peninsula at the **38th parallel. Kim Il Sung,** a communist, ruled the North; and **Syngman Rhee,** allied with the United States, controlled the South. In 1950, North Korean troops attacked South Korea. The United Nations forces stopped them along a line known as the **Pusan Perimeter,** then began advancing north. Mao sent troops to help the North Koreans. UN forces were pushed back south of the 38th parallel.

In 1953, both sides signed an armistice to end the fighting, but troops remained on both sides of the **demilitarized zone (DMZ).** Over time, South Korea enjoyed an economic boom and a rise in living standards, while communist North Korea's economy declined. Kim Il Sung's emphasis on self-reliance kept North Korea isolated and poor.

Review Questions

1. What was the effect of the Cultural Revolution?

_____

_____

2. How did the North Korean economy differ from the South Korean economy?

_____

_____

READING CHECK

What is the significance of the 38th parallel?

_____

_____

_____

VOCABULARY STRATEGY

What does the word *commune* mean in the underlined sentence? The terms *group home, community,* and *collective farm* are all synonyms of *commune.* Use the synonyms to help you figure out the meaning of *commune.*

READING SKILL

Summarize Summarize the effects of the Great Leap Forward on the Chinese people.

_____

_____

_____

© Pearson Education, Inc., publishing as Pearson Prentice Hall. All rights reserved.

Focus Question: What were the causes and effects of war in Southeast Asia, and what was the American role in this region?

As you read this section in your textbook, complete the flowchart below to summarize the events in Southeast Asia after World War II.

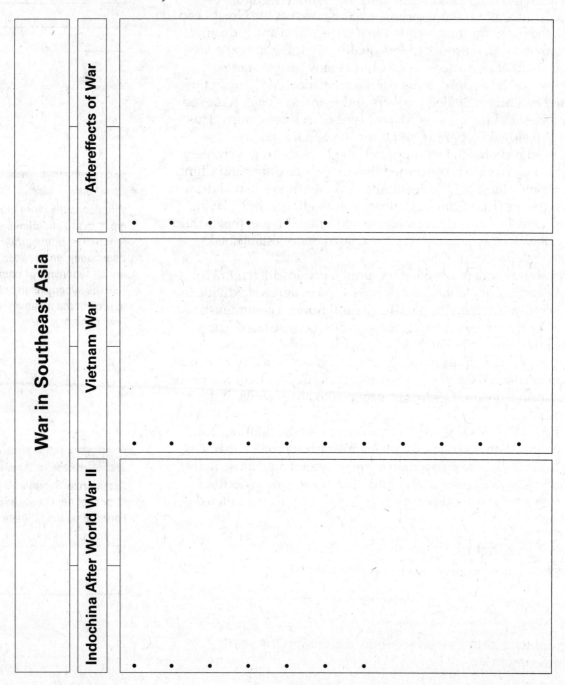

War in Southeast Asia

Aftereffects of War

Vietnam War

Indochina After World War II

© Pearson Education, Inc., publishing as Pearson Prentice Hall. All rights reserved.

CHAPTER 15
SECTION 4

Section Summary
WAR IN SOUTHEAST ASIA

In the 1800s, the French ruled the area in Southeast Asia called French Indochina. During World War II, Japan invaded that region, but faced resistance from **guerrillas.** After the war, the French tried to reestablish authority in Vietnam. However, forces led by communist leader **Ho Chi Minh** fought the colonialists. The French left Vietnam in 1954, after a Vietnamese victory at **Dienbienphu.** After that, Ho controlled the northern part of Vietnam while the United States supported the noncommunist government in the south.

Ho wanted to unite Vietnam. He provided aid to the National Liberation Front, or **Viet Cong,** a communist guerrilla organization in the south. American leaders saw Vietnam as an extension of the Cold War and developed the **domino theory.** This was the belief that if communists won in South Vietnam, then communism could spread to other governments in Southeast Asia. After a North Vietnamese attack on a U.S. Navy destroyer, Congress authorized the president to take military measures to prevent further communist aggression in Southeast Asia.

Despite massive American support, the South Vietnamese failed to defeat the Viet Cong and their North Vietnamese allies. During the **Tet Offensive,** the North Vietnamese attacked cities all over the south. Even though the communists were not able to hold any cities, it marked a turning point in U.S. public opinion. Upset by civilian deaths from the U.S. bombing of North Vietnam as well as growing American casualties, many Americans began to oppose the war. President Nixon came under increasing pressure to terminate the conflict. The Paris Peace Accord of 1973 established a ceasefire and American troops began to withdraw. Two years later communist North Vietnam conquered South Vietnam.

Neighboring Cambodia and Laos also ended up with communist governments. In Cambodia, guerrillas called the **Khmer Rouge** came to power. Led by the brutal dictator **Pol Pot,** their policies led to a genocide that killed about one third of the population. When Vietnam invaded Cambodia, the genocide ended. Pol Pot and the Khmer Rouge were forced to retreat. Communism did not spread any farther in Southeast Asia.

Review Questions

1. What was the domino theory?

_____

_____

2. Who were the Khmer Rouge and what role did they play in Cambodia?

_____

_____

READING CHECK

What was significant about the Tet Offensive?

_____

_____

_____

VOCABULARY STRATEGY

What does the word *terminate* mean in the underlined sentence? Note that the word is a verb. Ask yourself what action President Nixon was being pressured to take. Use this strategy to help you figure out what *terminate* means.

READING SKILL

Summarize Summarize U.S. involvement in Vietnam.

_____

_____

_____

© Pearson Education, Inc., publishing as Pearson Prentice Hall. All rights reserved.

Note Taking Study Guide
THE END OF THE COLD WAR

Focus Question: What were the causes and effects of the end of the Cold War?

As you read this section in your textbook, complete this flowchart to help you categorize events connected to the end of the Cold War. Some events have been completed for you.

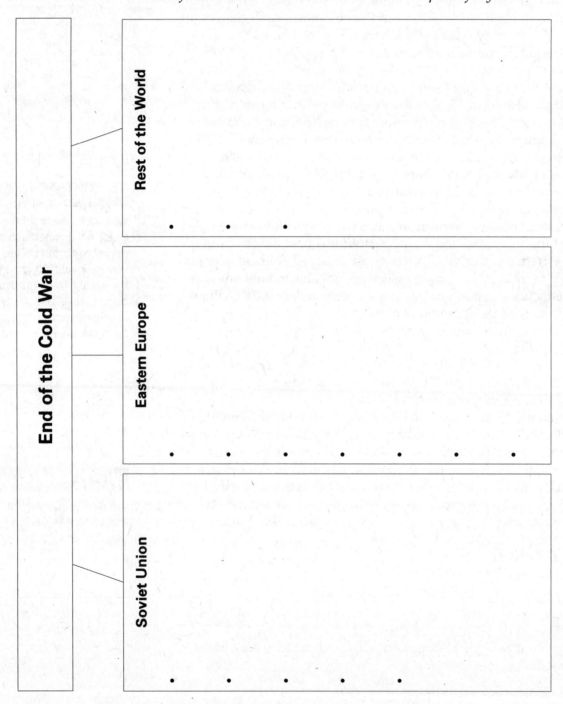

© Pearson Education, Inc., publishing as Pearson Prentice Hall. All rights reserved.

CHAPTER 15 SECTION 5

Section Summary

THE END OF THE COLD WAR

The Soviet Union emerged from World War II as a superpower, with control over many Eastern European countries. For many people, the country's superpower status brought few rewards. Consumer goods were inferior and workers were poorly paid. <u>Because workers had lifetime job security, there was little incentive to produce high-quality goods.</u> Still, there were some important technological successes. One example was *Sputnik I,* the first artificial satellite. Keeping up with the United States in an arms race also strained the economy. Then in 1979, Soviet forces invaded Afghanistan and became involved in a long war. The Soviets had few successes battling the **mujahedin,** or Muslim religious warriors, creating a crisis in morale in the USSR.

Then, new Soviet leader **Mikhail Gorbachev** urged reforms. He called for **glasnost.** He ended censorship and encouraged people to discuss the country's problems. Gorbachev also called for **perestroika,** or a restructuring of the government and economy. His policies, however, fed unrest across the Soviet empire.

Eastern Europeans demanded an end to Soviet rule. Previous attempts to defy the Soviets had failed. When Hungarians and Czechs challenged the communist rulers, military force subdued them. By the end of the 1980s, a powerful democracy movement was sweeping the region. In Poland, **Lech Walesa** led **Solidarity,** an independent, unlawful labor union demanding economic and political changes. When Gorbachev declared he would not interfere in Eastern European reforms, Solidarity was legalized. A year later, Walesa was elected president of Poland.

Meanwhile, East German leaders resisted reform, and thousands of East Germans fled to the West. In Czechoslovakia, **Václav Havel,** a dissident writer, was elected president. One by one, communist governments fell. Most changes happened peacefully, but Romanian dictator **Nicolae Ceausescu** refused to step down and he was executed. The Baltic States regained independence. By the end of 1991, the remaining Soviet republics had all formed independent nations. The Soviet Union ceased to exist after 69 years of communist rule.

In 1992, Czechoslovakia was divided into Slovakia and the Czech Republic. Additionally, some communist governments in Asia, such as China, instituted economic reforms.

Review Questions

1. What kinds of reforms did Gorbachev make?

_____

_____

2. What happened to the Soviet Union by the end of 1991?

_____

_____

READING CHECK

How did the arms race affect the Soviet economy?

_____

_____

_____

VOCABULARY STRATEGY

What does the word *incentive* mean in the underlined sentence? The words *motivation* and *reason* are synonyms of *incentive.* Use these synonyms to help you figure out the meaning of *incentive.*

READING SKILL

Categorize Which leaders mentioned in the summary supported reform and which leaders opposed reform?

_____

_____

_____

© Pearson Education, Inc., publishing as Pearson Prentice Hall. All rights reserved.

Focus Question: What were the consequences of independence in South Asia for the region and for the world?

As you read this section in your textbook, fill in the concept web below to identify causes and effects of events in South Asia.

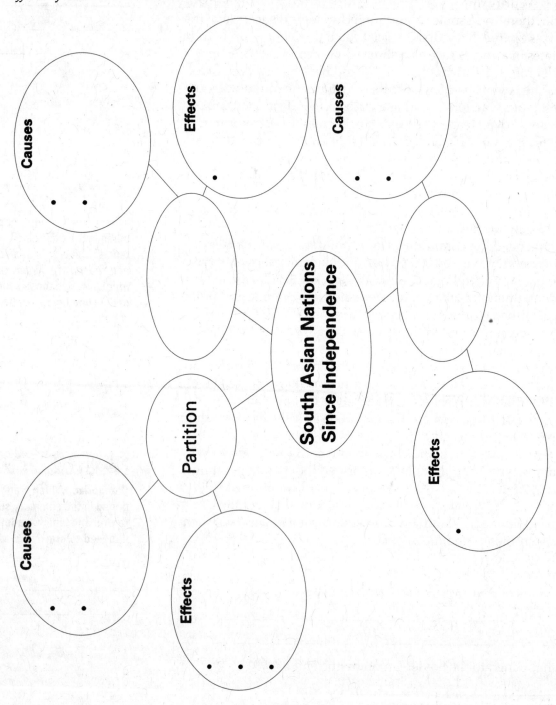

© Pearson Education, Inc., publishing as Pearson Prentice Hall. All rights reserved.

Section Summary
INDEPENDENT NATIONS OF SOUTH ASIA

In the 1940s, tensions between Hindus and Muslims in India led to violence. The ruling British decided that the only solution was a **partition,** or division, into a Muslim-majority Pakistan and a Hindu-majority India. After Pakistan and India gained their independence in 1947, Hindus in Pakistan fled to India, while Muslims in India fled to Pakistan. As they fled, Muslims, Hindus, and another religious group called **Sikhs** slaughtered one another.

Tensions have continued in the region. India and Pakistan have fought wars over **Kashmir,** a state with Muslim and Hindu populations. When India developed nuclear weapons, Pakistan began its own nuclear weapons program. In the island country of Sri Lanka, a majority are Buddhists. A Tamil-speaking Hindu minority on the island has fought for years for a separate Tamil nation.

In 1947, **Jawaharlal Nehru** became India's first prime minister. He tried to improve living conditions and end discrimination against **dalits,** or outcastes. Nehru's daughter, **Indira Gandhi,** became prime minister in 1966. While she was in office, Sikhs pressed for independence for the state of **Punjab.** In 1984, Sikh separatists occupied the **Golden Temple,** the holiest Sikh shrine. Gandhi sent troops to the temple, and thousands of Sikhs were killed. A few months later, Gandhi's Sikh bodyguards assassinated her.

In 1947, Pakistan was a divided country. A thousand miles separated West Pakistan from East Pakistan. West Pakistan dominated the nation's government. Most people in East Pakistan were Bengalis. They felt their government neglected their region. In 1971, Bengalis declared independence for East Pakistan under the name of **Bangladesh.** Pakistan tried to crush the rebels but was eventually compelled to recognize the independence of Bangladesh.

Pakistan has long lacked political stability. Islamic fundamentalists disagree with those who want a greater separation between religion and government. During the 1980s, the war in Afghanistan drove over a million Afghan refugees into Pakistan. Pakistan's Islamic fundamentalists gained power by forming ties with Afghan refugees.

Despite their differences, India and Pakistan helped organize a conference of newly independent states in 1955. This marked the birth of **nonalignment,** or political and diplomatic independence from the United States or the Soviet Union.

Review Questions

1. Why was Indira Gandhi assassinated?

_____

_____

2. Why did Bengalis want East Pakistan to be independent?

_____

_____

READING CHECK

What is nonalignment?

_____

_____

_____

VOCABULARY STRATEGY

What does the word *compelled* mean in the underlined sentence? *Compel* comes from a Latin word that means "to drive." If you substitute the word "driven" for *compelled* in the underlined sentence, it will help you figure out what *compelled* means.

READING SKILL

Identify Causes and Effects
What caused the British to partition India? What were some of the effects the partition had on Muslims and Hindus?

_____

_____

_____

© Pearson Education, Inc., publishing as Pearson Prentice Hall. All rights reserved.

CHAPTER 16 SECTION 2

Note Taking Study Guide

NEW NATIONS OF SOUTHEAST ASIA

Focus Question: What challenges did Southeast Asian nations face after winning independence?

As you read this section in your textbook, fill in the concept web below to understand the effects of recent historical processes in Southeast Asia.

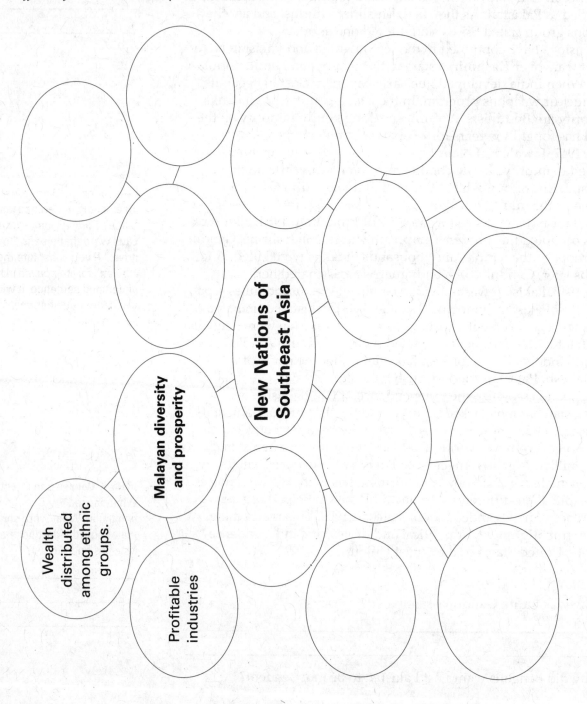

© Pearson Education, Inc., publishing as Pearson Prentice Hall. All rights reserved.

Section Summary
NEW NATIONS OF SOUTHEAST ASIA

Mainland Southeast Asia is a region of contrasts. Thailand and Malaysia have prospered as market economies. In Malaysia, people of Chinese and Indian descent have made the nation a leader in profitable industries. However, the government has also tried to include the Malay majority in the country's prosperity. By contrast, Myanmar, or Burma, has suffered under an **autocratic** government— a government that has unlimited power. The government has limited foreign trade, and living standards remain low. In 1990, elections were held in Myanmar, and a party that opposed military rule won. It was led by **Aung San Suu Kyi.** However, the military rejected the election results, and Suu Kyi was put under house arrest.

After World War II, Indonesia, formerly the Dutch East Indies, achieved its independence. Indonesia faced many obstacles to its unity. It consists of more than 13,000 islands. Javanese make up almost half of the population, but there are hundreds of ethnic groups. About 90 percent of Indonesians are Muslims, but the population includes Christians, Buddhists, and Hindus. After independence, Indonesia formed a democratic, parliamentary government under its first president, **Sukarno.** In 1966, an army general, **Suharto,** seized power and ruled as a dictator until he was forced to resign in 1998. Religious and ethnic tensions have fueled violence in parts of Indonesia. In 1975, Indonesia seized **East Timor,** a former Portuguese colony. The mostly Catholic East Timorese fought for independence, which they finally achieved in 2002.

In the Philippines, Catholics are the predominant religious group, but there is a Muslim minority in the south. In 1946, the Philippines gained freedom from United States control. Although the Filipino constitution established a democratic government, a wealthy elite controlled politics and the economy. **Ferdinand Marcos,** elected president in 1965, became a dictator and cracked down on basic freedoms. He even had **Benigno Aquino,** a popular rival, murdered. When **Corazon Aquino** was elected in 1986, Marcos tried to deny the results, but the people forced him to resign. Since then, democracy has struggled to survive in the Philippines. Communist and Muslim rebels continue to fight across the country.

Review Questions

1. What happened when Aung San Suu Kyi's party won the 1990 elections in Myanmar?

_____

_____

2. What are some obstacles to Indonesia's unity?

_____

_____

READING CHECK

What are the features of the autocratic government in Myanmar?

_____

_____

_____

VOCABULARY STRATEGY

What does *predominant* mean in the underlined sentence? Note that the second part of the sentence mentions another group that is a minority, or a smaller group. Use this context clue to help you figure out the meaning of *predominant.*

READING SKILL

Understand Effects What was the effect of Ferdinand Marcos' denial of the results of the 1986 election?

_____

_____

_____

© Pearson Education, Inc., publishing as Pearson Prentice Hall. All rights reserved.

Focus Question: What challenges did new African nations face?

As you read this section in your textbook, fill in the concept web below to keep track of the causes and effects of independence in Africa.

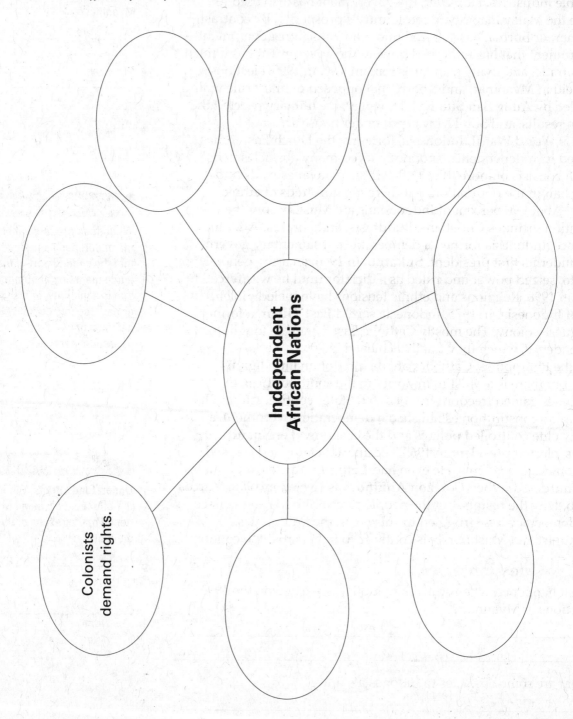

© Pearson Education, Inc., publishing as Pearson Prentice Hall. All rights reserved.

CHAPTER 16 SECTION 3

Section Summary
AFRICAN NATIONS GAIN INDEPENDENCE

Africa is a diverse continent. Vast **savannas,** or grasslands, cover much of it, but there are also rain forests and deserts. Diversity is reflected in the continent's history, people, languages, and traditions.

After World War II, many Africans demanded freedom from European powers. After gaining independence, some African nations enjoyed peace and democracy. Others faced civil wars, military rule, or corrupt dictators. European powers had drawn colonial boundaries without regard for Africa's ethnic groups. This led to ethnic conflict in many new nations once colonial powers withdrew.

In 1957, Gold Coast gained its freedom from Britain and took the name Ghana. The government of its first president, **Kwame Nkrumah,** eventually became corrupt, and Nkrumah was overthrown in a military **coup d'etat.** Other coups followed, but today Ghana is a democracy.

In Kenya, white settlers had passed laws to ensure their domination of the country. In the 1950s, rebels turned to guerrilla warfare, but the British crushed the rebellion. Kenya finally gained its independence in 1963. **Jomo Kenyatta,** a prominent independence leader, became the first president of the new country. In 2002, Kenya's first fair election removed the ruling party from office.

In Algeria, independence from France came only after a long war but was finally achieved in 1962. A coup in 1965 began a long period of military rule. When the government allowed free elections in 1992, an **Islamist** party won. The military rejected the results, and seven years of civil war followed. Although the fighting has ended, the country remains tense.

After the Congo became independent from Belgium, the copper-rich province of **Katanga** rebelled. The United Nations ended the rebellion in 1963. **Mobutu Sese Seko** ruled as a harsh military dictator from 1965 to 1997. Seven years of civil war ended with a cease-fire in 2003.

Nigeria won its independence in 1960, but regional, ethnic, and religious differences soon led to conflict. In 1966, the Ibo people in the southeast declared independence as the Republic of **Biafra.** After three years of fighting, Nigeria's military ended Biafra's independence. A series of dictators then ruled, but Nigeria returned to democracy in 1999.

Review Questions

1. Why was the first president of Ghana overthrown?

_____

_____

2. What country did the Ibo people of Nigeria try to establish?

_____

_____

READING CHECK

What is a coup d'etat?

_____

_____

_____

VOCABULARY STRATEGY

What does the word *ensure* mean in the underlined sentence? The prefix *en-* means to "make" or "cause to be." Think about what the root word, *sure,* means. Use these clues about word parts to help you understand the meaning of *ensure.*

READING SKILL

Identify Causes and Effects
How did past decisions made by European powers cause ethnic conflict in many new African nations?

_____

_____

_____

© Pearson Education, Inc., publishing as Pearson Prentice Hall. All rights reserved.

Focus Question: What are the main similarities and differences among Middle Eastern nations?

As you read this section in your textbook, fill in the concept web below to identify causes and effects of events in the Middle East since 1945.

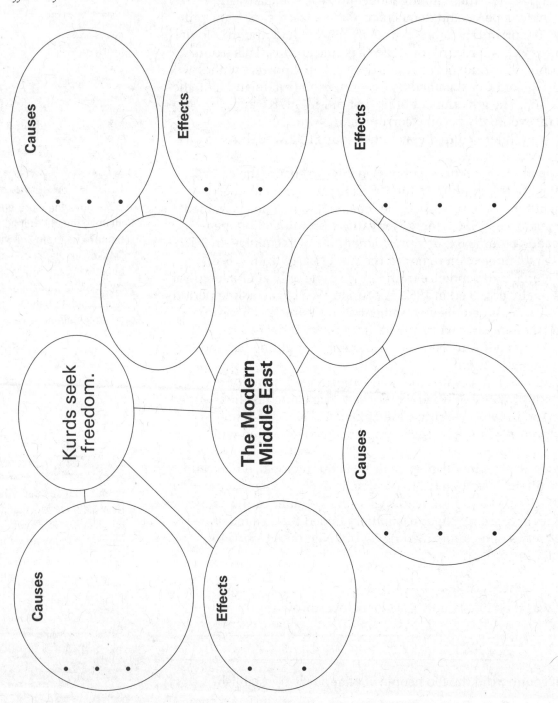

© Pearson Education, Inc., publishing as Pearson Prentice Hall. All rights reserved.

Name_____ Class_____ Date_____

Section Summary
THE MODERN MIDDLE EAST

Most of the people in the Middle East are Muslims, but there are also Christian communities and the predominantly Jewish nation of Israel. Most countries also have large ethnic or religious minorities. The Kurds are an example of an ethnic minority. They live in Iran, Iraq, Syria, and Turkey and have faced discrimination in each country.

The Holocaust created support for a Jewish homeland after World War II. In 1947, the UN drew up a plan to divide Palestine into an Arab and a Jewish state. In 1948, Jews proclaimed the independent state of Israel. This led to Arab-Israeli conflicts that forced 700,000 Palestinians from their homes. Despite the conflicts, Israel has developed rapidly due to a skilled workforce. Kibbutzim work on what is called a **kibbutz,** or collective farm.

Resources and religion have led to conflicts in the Middle East. The region has the world's largest oil and gas reserves. As a result, it has strategic importance. Some Middle Eastern countries have adopted **secular,** or non-religious, government and laws. However, many Muslim leaders argue that a renewed commitment to Islamic doctrine is needed. In Iran and Saudi Arabia, women are required to wear **hejab,** the traditional Muslim garments.

Egypt, the most populous Arab country, is important because it controls the **Suez Canal.** Under **Gamal Abdel Nasser,** Egypt fought two unsuccessful wars against Israel. His successor, **Anwar Sadat,** made peace with Israel. Islamists were angry about government corruption and the failure to end poverty. In 1981, Sadat was assassinated by Muslim fundamentalists.

In Iran, Shah Mohammad Reza Pahlavi ruled with the support of the United States, which helped oust one of his opponents, **Mohammad Mosaddeq.** The shah's secret police terrorized critics. In the 1970s, the shah's enemies rallied behind Ayatollah **Ruhollah Khomeini.** Protests forced the shah into exile, and Khomeini established an Islamic **theocracy,** or government ruled by religious leaders.

Saudi Arabia has the world's largest oil reserves and is the location of Islam's holy land. Kings from the Sa'ud family have ruled Saudi Arabia since the 1920s. Fundamentalists have criticized the kingdom's close ties to Western nations, and some opponents have adopted violent tactics that threaten to disrupt the Saudi oil industry.

Review Questions
1. What makes the Middle East of strategic importance?

_____

_____

2. Why have some Islamic fundamentalists criticized the Saudis?

_____

_____

READING CHECK

What is a theocracy?

_____

_____

_____

VOCABULARY STRATEGY

What does the word *doctrine* mean in the underlined sentence? The words *policy, dogma,* and *tenet* are all synonyms of doctrine. Use what you may know about these synonyms to help you figure out the meaning of the word *doctrine.*

READING SKILL

Identify Causes and Effects
What effect did the proclamation of an independent state of Israel have on Palestinians?

_____

_____

_____

© Pearson Education, Inc., publishing as Pearson Prentice Hall. All rights reserved.

CHAPTER
17
SECTION 1

Note Taking Study Guide

CONFLICTS DIVIDE NATIONS

Focus Question: Why have ethnic and religious conflicts divided some nations?

As you read this section in your textbook, fill in the flowchart below to help you recognize the sequence of events that took place in Northern Ireland, Chechnya, and Yugoslavia.

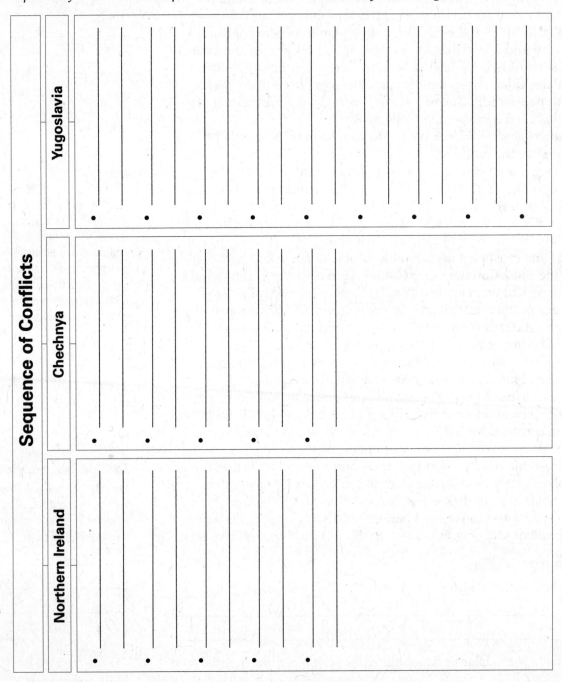

© Pearson Education, Inc., publishing as Pearson Prentice Hall. All rights reserved.

CHAPTER 17 SECTION 2

Section Summary
STRUGGLES IN AFRICA

In the 1950s and 1960s, many new nations won independence in Africa. Several other African nations suffered internal conflicts and civil wars. In 1910, South Africa achieved self-rule from Britain. Most civil rights, however, were limited to white settlers. The black majority had few rights under a legal system of racial segregation called **apartheid.** Under apartheid, nonwhites faced many restrictions. <u>For example, laws banned marriages between races and stipulated segregated restaurants, beaches, and schools.</u>

The **African National Congress (ANC)** opposed apartheid and led the struggle for majority rule. In 1960 police gunned down 69 people during a protest in **Sharpeville,** a black township. The government then outlawed the ANC. **Nelson Mandela,** an ANC leader, was sentenced to life imprisonment.

In the 1980s, international demands for an end to apartheid and for Mandela's release increased. In 1984, Bishop **Desmond Tutu** won the Nobel Peace Prize for his nonviolent opposition to apartheid. In 1990, South African president **F.W. de Klerk** ended apartheid and freed Mandela, who was elected president in 1994.

South Africa's neighbors also experienced long conflicts to attain independence. Portugal granted independence to Angola and Mozambique in 1975. South Africa and the United States saw the new nations as threats because some liberation leaders had ties to the ANC or the Soviet Union.

After independence, ethnic conflicts plagued many nations. Historic resentments divided nations, and regional rivalries fed ethnic violence. In Rwanda, one of Africa's deadliest wars occurred. There, the **Hutus** were the majority, but the minority **Tutsis** dominated the country. In 1994, extremist Hutus slaughtered about 800,000 Tutsis and moderate Hutus. Another 3 million Rwandans lost their homes. In response, world leaders pledged to stop genocide wherever it may occur. Their power to do this, however, was limited. In Sudan, non-Muslim, non-Arab rebels in the south battled Arab Muslims from the north. This war, drought, and famine caused millions of deaths. Finally, southern rebels signed a peace agreement in 2004. In the same year, however, ethnic conflict spread to Darfur in western Sudan. This conflict raised fears of a new genocide.

Review Questions

1. Describe conditions under apartheid in South Africa.

_____

_____

2. What led to deadly war in Rwanda?

_____

_____

READING CHECK

Which two African countries gained independence from Portugal?

_____

_____

_____

VOCABULARY STRATEGY

What does the word *stipulated* mean in the underlined sentence? Note that *stipulated* refers to laws. The previous sentence has a reference to restrictions that non-whites faced. Use these context clues to help you understand the meaning of the word *stipulated*.

READING SKILL

Recognize Sequence Did the South African government outlaw the ANC before or after the protest in Sharpeville?

_____

_____

_____

© Pearson Education, Inc., publishing as Pearson Prentice Hall. All rights reserved.

Focus Question: What are the causes of conflict in the Middle East?

As you read the section in your textbook, use the flowchart to record the sequence of events relating to the conflicts in the Middle East.

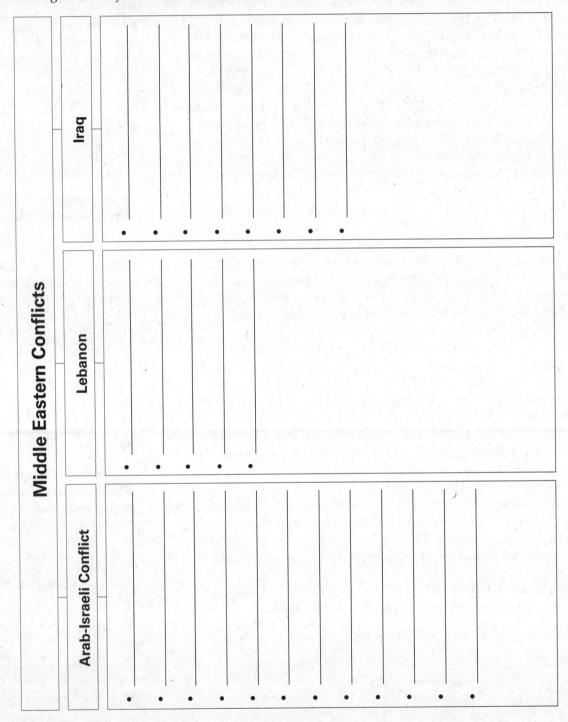

© Pearson Education, Inc., publishing as Pearson Prentice Hall. All rights reserved.

Section Summary
CONFLICTS IN THE MIDDLE EAST

For decades, the Middle East has been the location of conflict. Modern Israel was created in 1948 on land that had belonged to Palestinian Arabs. As a result, there has been repeated war and violence. In several wars against Egypt and others, Israel gained more land. This is called the **occupied territories.**

The Palestine Liberation Organization, led by **Yasir Arafat,** fought against the Israelis. In the occupied territories, Palestinians launched uprisings called **intifadas.** In addition, suicide bombers spread terror inside Israel. The Israelis responded with armed force, and Palestinian bitterness increased. Leaders, such as Israeli Prime Minister **Yitzhak Rabin,** pushed for peace. There were many stumbling blocks, however, such as disagreements over **Jerusalem,** a city sacred to Jews, Christians, and Muslims. During the early 2000s, new steps toward peace offered some hope, but serious obstacles remained.

Lebanon is home to diverse ethnic and religious groups. The government depended on a delicate balance among Arab Christians, Sunni Muslims, Shiite Muslims, and Druze. In 1975, Christian and Muslim **militias** battled each other, and both Israel and Syria invaded. By 1990, however, peace had been restored.

Conflicts also plagued Iraq. Iraq's Sunni Muslim minority dominated the country for centuries. The Kurdish minority and Shiite Muslim majority were excluded from power. In 1979 **Saddam Hussein** took power as a dictator. He fought a prolonged war against neighboring Iran in the 1980s. In 1990, Iraq invaded Kuwait. In response, the United States led a coalition against that invasion. In the Gulf War that ensued, Kuwait was liberated and Iraqi forces were crushed. Saddam Hussein remained in power and used terror to impose his will. The United States, France, and Britain set up **no-fly zones** to protect the Kurds and Shiites. The UN worked to keep Saddam Hussein from building biological, nuclear, or chemical weapons, called **weapons of mass destruction (WMDs).**

In 2003, the United States led a coalition that invaded Iraq and overthrew Saddam Hussein. Iraqi **insurgents** fought against the occupation that followed. In 2005, national elections were held for the first time.

Review Questions
1. How did Israel come to control the occupied territories?

_____

_____

2. What were the results of the Gulf War in 1990?

_____

_____

READING CHECK

Which groups in Iraq were excluded from power?

_____

_____

_____

VOCABULARY STRATEGY

What does the word *diverse* mean in the underlined sentence? Notice how in the next sentence four ethnic groups are mentioned. Use this context clue to help you understand the meaning of *diverse.*

READING SKILL

Recognize Sequence Circle the phrase in the sentence below that signals sequence.

In 1990, Iraq invaded Kuwait. In response, the United States led a coalition against the invasion.

© Pearson Education, Inc., publishing as Pearson Prentice Hall. All rights reserved.

CHAPTER 18 SECTION 1

Note Taking Study Guide
THE CHALLENGES OF DEVELOPMENT

Focus Question: How have the nations of the developing world tried to build better lives for their people?

As you read this section in your textbook, complete the chart below with supporting details from the text about economic development and developing countries.

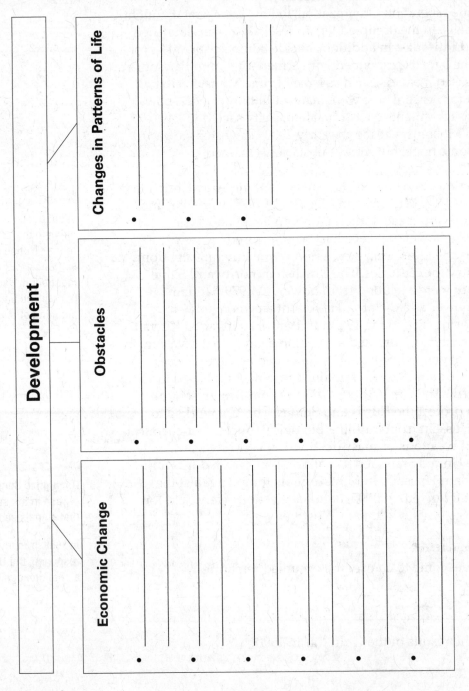

© Pearson Education, Inc., publishing as Pearson Prentice Hall. All rights reserved.

CHAPTER 18 SECTION 1

Section Summary

THE CHALLENGES OF DEVELOPMENT

After World War II, a central goal in Africa, Asia, and Latin America was **development,** or creating a more advanced economy and higher living standards. Nations that are working toward this are referred to as the **developing world.** They are also called the global South, because most of these nations are south of the Tropic of Cancer. Most industrialized nations are north of the Tropic of Cancer, so they are sometimes called the global North. Nations of the global South have tried to develop economically by improving their agriculture and industry. They have also built schools to increase **literacy.**

To pay for development, many countries in the global South procured large loans from industrialized nations. For centuries, most people in the global South had lived and worked in **traditional economies.** After gaining independence from European colonists, some of these countries experimented with government-led command economies. However, when these countries had trouble paying off their loans, lenders from the global North required many of them to change to market economies. Now many developing nations depend on the global North for investment and exports.

Beginning in the 1950s, improved seeds, pesticides, and mechanical equipment led to a **Green Revolution** in many parts of the developing world. This increased agricultural production, feeding many more people. It also benefited large landowners at the expense of small farmers. These farmers sold their land and moved to cities.

The global South still faces many challenges. Some developing nations produce only one export product. If prices for that product drop, their economies suffer. Also, the population in many of these countries has grown rapidly. Many people are caught in a cycle of poverty. When families are forced to move to cities, they often find only low-paying jobs. As a result, many children must work to help support their families. With so many moving to cities, many people are forced to live in crowded and dangerous **shantytowns.**

Economic development has brought great changes to the developing world. In many countries, women have greater equality. However, some religious **fundamentalists** oppose these changes and have called for a return to the basic values of their faiths.

Review Questions

1. What happened when nations in the global South had trouble repaying their loans?

_____

_____

2. What problems do people in the developing world often face when they move to cities?

_____

_____

READING CHECK

What is development?

_____

_____

_____

VOCABULARY STRATEGY

What does the word *procured* mean in the underlined sentence? Notice that *procured* refers to loans. Use this clue to help you figure out the meaning of the word *procured.*

READING SKILL

Identify Supporting Details Record details that support this statement: "The global South faces many challenges."

_____

_____

_____

© Pearson Education, Inc., publishing as Pearson Prentice Hall. All rights reserved.

Note Taking Study Guide

AFRICA SEEKS A BETTER FUTURE

Focus Question: What challenges have African nations faced in their effort to develop their economies?

As you read this section in your textbook, complete the concept web below to record the main ideas about challenges faced by African nations, and details that support those main ideas.

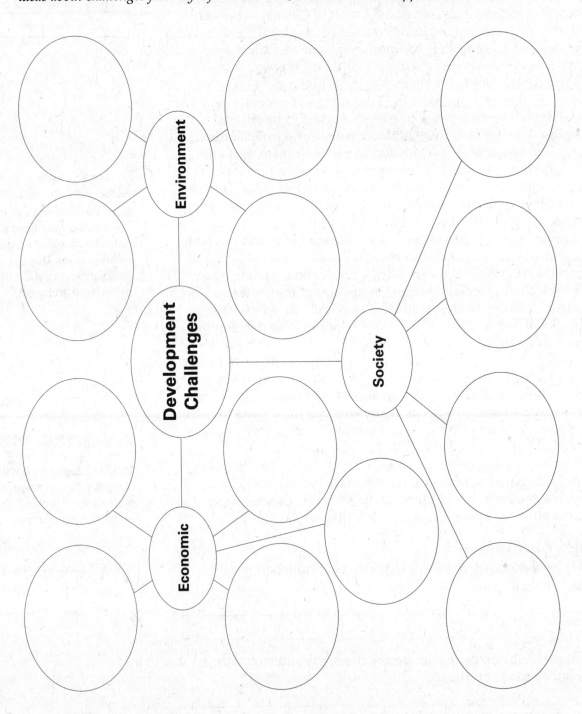

© Pearson Education, Inc., publishing as Pearson Prentice Hall. All rights reserved.

Section Summary
AFRICA SEEKS A BETTER FUTURE

After World War II, African nations had little capital to invest, so they had to make difficult economic choices. Some nations chose **socialism,** a system in which the government controls parts of the economy. The leaders of these governments hoped to end foreign influence in their countries and to close the gap between the rich and the poor. However, socialism sometimes led to large, inefficient bureaucracies. Other nations relied on capitalism, or market economies. These economies were often more efficient, but foreign owners of businesses took profits out of the country. Some governments tried to fund development by growing crops for export, rather than food crops. However, this forced them to import food to replace the food crops. <u>Governments then had to subsidize part of the cost of importing food from overseas.</u>

African nations faced many obstacles to development. Droughts led to famine in parts of Africa. This was especially true in the Sahel, where overgrazing and farming led to **desertification.** People in African nations also faced the devastating disease AIDS. In the early 2000s, more than 2 million Africans died of the disease each year. **Urbanization** has also created problems in Africa. This shift from rural areas to cities has meant hardship for many and has weakened traditional cultures and ethnic ties. However, in West Africa, the growth of urban markets has increased opportunities for women.

Another concern in Africa is environmental threats. Nearly 70 percent of Africa's animal habitats have been destroyed, causing many animals to become **endangered species.** Other animal species are being killed for their tusks or fur. One environmental activist, **Wangari Maathai,** has fought back by starting the Green Belt Movement. This organization promotes reforestation. It also helps local women with projects of **sustainable development** that aim to provide lasting benefits for future generations.

A close look at Tanzania reveals the problems that many African counties have faced. In the 1960s, the government embraced "African socialism." However, attempts to build on African traditions of cooperation failed to increase agricultural production. In 1985, new leaders introduced economic reforms. However, Tanzania remains poor and has had to rely on foreign loans to avoid economic crisis.

Review Questions

1. Why did some African nations choose socialism?

_____

_____

2. Why are many animal species in Africa endangered?

_____

_____

READING CHECK

What is urbanization?

_____

_____

_____

VOCABULARY STRATEGY

What does the word *subsidize* mean in the underlined sentence? *Subsidize* comes from a Latin word that means "aid" or "support." Use this clue to help you figure out the meaning of the word *subsidize*.

READING SKILL

Identify Main Ideas What is the main idea of this Summary?

_____

_____

_____

© Pearson Education, Inc., publishing as Pearson Prentice Hall. All rights reserved.

CHAPTER 18
SECTION 3

Note Taking Study Guide
CHINA AND INDIA: TWO GIANTS OF ASIA

Focus Question: How do China and India compare in building strong economies and democratic governments?

As you read this section in your textbook, complete the table below to record the main ideas about reform and change in China and India.

Reform and Change in China and India

Type	China	India
Economic	• Free market • • • • • • •	• • • • •
Political	• • •	• • •

© Pearson Education, Inc., publishing as Pearson Prentice Hall. All rights reserved.

CHAPTER 18 SECTION 3

Section Summary

CHINA AND INDIA: TWO GIANTS OF ASIA

After Mao Zedong died, moderate leaders took control of China. **Deng Xiaoping** began a program called the Four Modernizations, which allowed some features of a free-market economy. Some private ownership of property was permitted, and entrepreneurs could set up businesses. Farmers were allowed to sell surplus produce and keep the profits. Foreign investment was also welcomed. These reforms brought a surge of economic growth, although a gap developed between poor farmers and wealthy city dwellers. After 30 years of reforms, China's economic output quadrupled.

Despite these economic reforms, however, Communist leaders refused to allow more political freedom. Demonstrators seeking democratic reforms occupied **Tiananmen Square** in Beijing in May 1989. When the demonstrators refused to disperse, the government sent in troops and tanks. Thousands were killed or wounded.

China continues to face many challenges. Its population is the largest in the world. The government started the **one-child policy** to prevent population growth from hurting economic development. Population growth slowed. Many rural workers have moved to cities, but they often live in poverty there. Pollution and HIV/AIDS are also problems. Critics of the government are jailed, and human rights abuses continue.

By contrast, India is the world's largest democracy. After gaining independence, India's government adopted a command economy, but development was uneven. The Green Revolution in the 1960s improved crop output, but most farmers continued to use traditional methods. In the 1980s, India shifted toward a free-market system. By the 1990s, several Indian industries were expanding rapidly.

Despite these improvements, India's population growth has hurt efforts to improve living conditions. The Indian government backed family planning, but it had limited success. More than one-third of Indians live below the poverty line. Many rural families moved to overcrowded cities like **Kolkata** and **Mumbai.** To help the urban poor, **Mother Teresa** founded the Missionaries of Charity.

Changes in India have brought improvements for India's lowest social castes and women. India's constitution bans discrimination against **dalits**, people in the lowest caste, but prejudice persists. The constitution also grants equal rights to women.

Review Questions

1. What impact have economic reforms had in China?

_____

_____

2. Name two groups that have benefited from changes in India.

_____

_____

READING CHECK

Which country, India or China, has had more success in limiting population growth?

_____

_____

_____

VOCABULARY STRATEGY

What does the word *disperse* mean in the underlined sentence? Notice that demonstrators occupied, or gathered in, Tiananmen Square and then refused to *disperse.* Use this clue to help you figure out the meaning of the word *disperse.*

READING SKILL

Identify Main Ideas In your own words, write the main idea of the first paragraph of this Summary.

_____

_____

_____

© Pearson Education, Inc., publishing as Pearson Prentice Hall. All rights reserved.

CHAPTER 18 SECTION 4

Note Taking Study Guide

LATIN AMERICA BUILDS DEMOCRACY

Focus Question: What challenges have Latin American nations faced in recent decades in their struggle for democracy and prosperity?

As you read this section in your textbook, complete this outline to identify the main ideas and supporting details about challenges faced by Latin American nations.

I. Economic and Social Forces

   A. Society

      1. _____

      2. _____

      3. _____

      4. _____

   B. _____

      1. _____

      2. _____

      3. _____

      4. _____

II. _____

   A. _____

      1. _____

      2. _____

      3. _____

   B. _____

      1. _____

      2. _____

   C. _____

      1. _____

      2. _____

      3. _____

      4. _____

      5. _____

      6. _____

      7. _____

(Outline continues on the next page.)

© Pearson Education, Inc., publishing as Pearson Prentice Hall. All rights reserved.

(Continued from page 162)

D. _____
   1. _____
   2. _____
E. _____
   1. _____
   2. _____
III. _____
   A. _____
      1. _____
      2. _____
   B. _____
      1. _____
      2. _____
      3. _____
      4. _____
      5. _____

© Pearson Education, Inc., publishing as Pearson Prentice Hall. All rights reserved.

CHAPTER 18 SECTION 4 — Section Summary

LATIN AMERICA BUILDS DEMOCRACY

READING CHECK

What is liberation theology?

_____

_____

_____

VOCABULARY STRATEGY

What does the word *alleged* mean in the underlined sentence? This verb is often used in legal proceedings. The noun form is *allegation*. An *allegation* is "an assertion made without proof." Use these clues to help you understand the meaning of *alleged*.

READING SKILL

Identify Main Ideas and Supporting Details Outline the last paragraph in the Summary on the lines below.

_____

_____

_____

_____

_____

_____

In the 1950s and 1960s, many governments in Latin America encouraged industries to manufacture goods that had previously been imported. This is called **import substitution.** More recently, government policies have focused on producing goods for export. Governments have also tried to open more land to farming, but much of the best land belongs to large **agribusinesses.** In many countries, a few people control the land and businesses, and wealth is distributed unevenly. Another problem is population growth, which has contributed to poverty. Many religious leaders have worked for justice and an end to poverty in a movement known as **liberation theology.**

Because of poverty and inequality, democracy has been difficult to achieve in Latin America. Between the 1950s and 1970s, military leaders seized power in Argentina, Brazil, Chile, and other countries. From the 1960s to the 1990s, civil wars shook parts of Central America. In Guatemala, the military targeted the **indigenous** population and slaughtered thousands of Native Americans.

The United States has had a powerful influence in Latin America. It has dominated the **Organization of American States (OAS).** During the Cold War, the United States backed dictators who were anti-communist. When socialist rebels called **Sandinistas** came to power in Nicaragua, the United States supported the **contras,** guerrillas who fought the Sandinistas. The United States has also pressed Latin American governments to help stop the drug trade. Many Latin Americans alleged that the problem was not in Latin America but was based on the demand for drugs in the United States.

By the 1990s, democratic reforms led to free elections in many countries. In Mexico, the Institutional Revolutionary Party (PRI) had dominated the government since the 1920s. However, in 2000, an opposition candidate was elected president. Argentina experienced 50 years of political upheavals beginning in the 1930s. **Juan Perón,** Argentina's president from 1946 to 1955, enjoyed great support from workers but was ousted in a military coup. The military seized control again in 1976 and murdered or kidnapped thousands. Mothers whose sons and daughters were missing protested and became known as the **Mothers of the Plaza de Mayo.** By 1983, the military was forced to allow elections.

Review Questions

1. Why was democracy difficult to achieve in Latin America?

_____

_____

2. Why did the United States support dictators in Latin America during the Cold War?

_____

_____

© Pearson Education, Inc., publishing as Pearson Prentice Hall. All rights reserved.

Note Taking Study Guide
INDUSTRIALIZED NATIONS AFTER THE COLD WAR

Focus Question: How did the end of the Cold War affect industrialized nations and regions around the world?

As you read this section in your textbook, complete the chart below to compare and contrast developments in industrialized nations after the Cold War.

Asia
-

Russia/United States

Russia
-

United States
-

Europe
- 1991 — Germany is reunified.

© Pearson Education, Inc., publishing as Pearson Prentice Hall. All rights reserved.

CHAPTER 19 SECTION 1

Section Summary

INDUSTRIALIZED NATIONS AFTER THE COLD WAR

READING CHECK

Which four Pacific Rim countries are called the "Asian tigers"?

_____

_____

_____

VOCABULARY STRATEGY

What does the word *inflation* mean in the underlined sentence? Think about what happens when you *inflate* a tire. In this sentence, *inflation* refers to prices. If prices are *inflated*, would you expect them to be higher or lower? Use these clues to help you understand the meaning of *inflation*.

READING SKILL

Compare and Contrast Compare and contrast the U.S. economy in the early 1990s with the economy in the early 2000s.

_____

_____

_____

The beginning of a new global economy began with the end of the Cold War. The division between communist Eastern and democratic Western Europe crumbled. Business and travel became easier. At the same time, new challenges emerged, including a rise in unemployment and in immigration from the developing world. One exciting change was the reunification of Germany. However, East Germany's economy was weak and had to be modernized.

In the 1990s, the European Economic Community became the **European Union** (EU). The **euro** soon became the common currency for most of Western Europe. By the early 2000s, more than a dozen countries had joined the EU, including some Eastern European nations. The expanded EU allowed Europe to compete economically with the United States and Japan. However, older members of the EU worried that the weak economies of Eastern European nations might harm the EU. Most Eastern European nations wanted to join NATO, too.

After the breakup of the Soviet Union, Russia struggled to forge a market economy. Unemployment and prices soared, and criminals flourished. In 1998, Russia **defaulted** on much of its foreign debt. <u>High inflation and the collapse of the Russian currency forced banks and businesses to close.</u> When **Vladimir Putin** became president in 2000, he promised to end corruption and strengthen Russia's economy. However, he also increased government power at the expense of civil liberties.

After the Cold War, the United States became the world's only superpower. It waged wars in the Middle East and started peacekeeping operations in Haiti and the former Yugoslavia. An economic boom in the 1990s produced a budget **surplus** in the United States. Within a decade, however, slow economic growth and soaring military expenses led to huge budget **deficits.**

The **Pacific Rim** nations have become a rising force in the global economy. Following World War II, Japan became an economic powerhouse and dominated this region. However, by the 1990s, Japan's economy began to suffer, and Taiwan, Hong Kong, Singapore, and South Korea surged ahead. These "Asian tigers" have achieved economic success, due in part to low wages, long hours, and other worker sacrifices.

Review Questions

1. When did the global economy begin to develop?

_____

_____

2. What economic challenges did Russia face after the breakup of the Soviet Union?

_____

_____

© Pearson Education, Inc., publishing as Pearson Prentice Hall. All rights reserved.

CHAPTER
19
SECTION 2

Note Taking Study Guide
GLOBALIZATION

Focus Question: How is globalization affecting economies and societies around the world?

As you read this section in your textbook, use the Venn diagram to compare the effects of globalization on developed and developing nations.

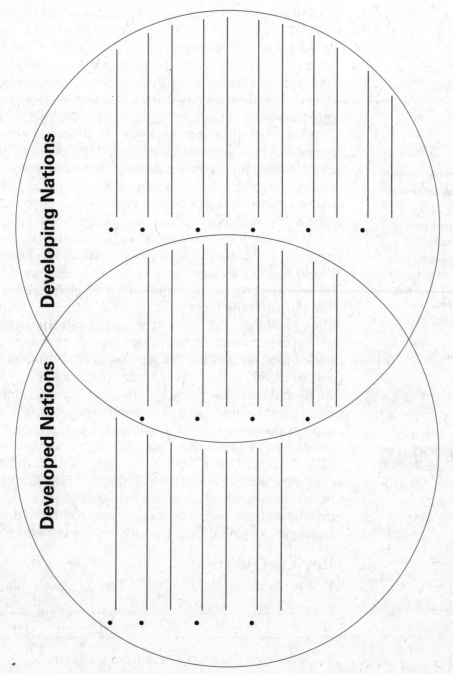

© Pearson Education, Inc., publishing as Pearson Prentice Hall. All rights reserved.

CHAPTER 19 SECTION 2

Section Summary
GLOBALIZATION

READING CHECK

What is globalization?

_____

_____

_____

Globalization defines the post-Cold War world. It is the process by which national economies, politics, and cultures become integrated with those of other nations. One effect of globalization is economic **interdependence.** This means that countries depend on one another for goods, resources, knowledge, and labor.

Improvements in transportation and communication, the spread of democracy, and the rise of free trade have made the world more interdependent. Developed nations control much of the world's capital, trade, and technology. Yet they rely on workers in developing countries, to which they **outsource** jobs to save money or increase efficiency. Globalization has also encouraged the rise of **multinational corporations** that have branches and assets in many countries.

One effect of interdependence is that an economic crisis in one region can have a worldwide impact. For example, any change to the global oil supply affects economies all around the world. Another example is debt. Poor nations need to borrow capital from rich nations in order to modernize. When poor nations cannot repay their debts, both poor nations and rich nations are hurt.

VOCABULARY STRATEGY

What does the word *assets* mean in the underlined sentence? Think about what it means if someone says that you are an *asset* to the team. Use this clue to help you figure out the meaning of *assets.*

Many international organizations and treaties make global trade possible. The United Nations deals with a broad range of issues. The World Bank gives loans and advice to developing nations. The International Monetary Fund promotes global economic growth. The **World Trade Organization (WTO)** tries to ensure that trade flows smoothly and freely. It opposes **protectionism**—the use of tariffs to protect a country's industries from competition. Regional trade **blocs,** such as the EU in Europe, NAFTA in North America, and APEC in Asia, promote trade within regions.

Global trade has many benefits. It brings consumers a greater variety of goods and services. It generally keeps prices lower. It also exposes people to new ideas and technology. Nations involved in free trade often become more democratic. However, some people oppose globalization of trade. They claim that rich countries exploit poor countries. Some believe that globalization hurts indigenous peoples by taking away their lands and disrupting their cultures. Others say that the emphasis on profits encourages too-rapid development. This endangers **sustainability,** thereby threatening future generations.

READING SKILL

Compare and Contrast Compare and contrast the effect of borrowing capital on rich and poor nations.

_____

_____

_____

Review Questions

1. What is the goal of the World Trade Organization?

_____

_____

2. How do consumers benefit from global trade?

_____

_____

© Pearson Education, Inc., publishing as Pearson Prentice Hall. All rights reserved.

Note Taking Study Guide

SOCIAL AND ENVIRONMENTAL CHALLENGES

Focus Question: How do poverty, disease, and environmental challenges affect people around the world today?

As you read this section in your textbook, complete the chart below to compare aspects of globalization.

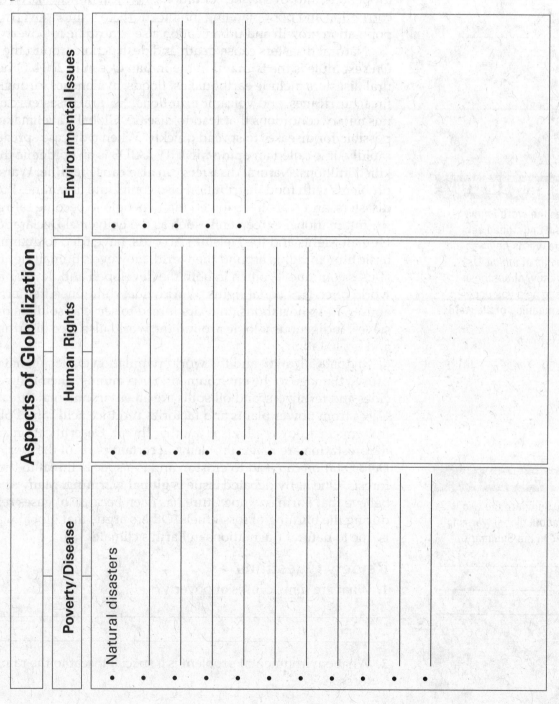

Aspects of Globalization

Environmental Issues
-
-
-
-
-

Human Rights
-
-
-
-
-
-

Poverty/Disease
- Natural disasters
-
-
-
-
-
-
-
-
-

© Pearson Education, Inc., publishing as Pearson Prentice Hall. All rights reserved.

CHAPTER 19 SECTION 3

Section Summary
SOCIAL AND ENVIRONMENTAL CHALLENGES

READING CHECK

What is an epidemic?

_____

_____

_____

VOCABULARY STRATEGY

What does the word *inhibit* mean in the underlined sentence? The words *help* and *aid* are antonyms of *inhibit*. Use what you know about these antonyms to help you understand the meaning of the word *inhibit*.

READING SKILL

Compare Compare the two theories about global warming mentioned in the Summary.

_____

_____

_____

Poverty, disasters, and disease are still challenges today. The gap between rich and poor nations is growing. Half the world's population earns less than $2 a day. Poverty is a complex issue with many causes. Many poor nations owe billions in debt and have little money to spend to improve living conditions. Political upheavals, civil war, corruption and poor planning inhibit efforts to reduce poverty. Rapid population growth and urbanization also contribute to poverty.

Natural disasters cause death and destruction around the world. One example is the **tsunami** in the Indian Ocean in 2004. Other natural disasters include earthquakes, floods, avalanches, droughts, fires, hurricanes, and volcanic eruptions. Natural disasters can cause unsanitary conditions that lead to disease. Global travel makes it possible for diseases to spread quickly. When a disease spreads rapidly, it is called an **epidemic.** HIV/AIDS is an epidemic that has killed millions. Natural disasters can also cause **famine.** Wars and problems with food distribution also contribute to famine. Poverty, disasters, and wars have forced many people to become **refugees.**

International agreements, such as the Universal Declaration of Human Rights and the Helsinki Accords, have tried to guarantee basic human rights around the world. However, human rights abuses continue. Women in both the developed and developing world often lack equal rights. Worldwide, children suffer terrible abuses. In some nations, they are forced to serve as soldiers or slaves. Indigenous people around the world also face discrimination and exploitation.

Industrialization and the world population explosion have caused damage to the environment. Strip mining, chemical pesticides and fertilizers, and oil spills are all environmental threats. Gases from power plants and factories produce **acid rain.** Pollution from nuclear power plants is another threat. Desertification and **deforestation** are major problems in certain parts of the world. Deforestation can lead to **erosion** and is a special threat to the rain forests. One hotly debated issue is **global warming.** Many scientists believe that Earth's temperature has risen because of gases released during the burning of fossil fuels. Others argue that global warming is due to natural fluctuations in Earth's climate.

Review Questions

1. What are some causes of poverty?

_____

_____

2. What environmental problem is a special threat to the rain forests?

_____

_____

© Pearson Education, Inc., publishing as Pearson Prentice Hall. All rights reserved.

CHAPTER 19 SECTION 4

Note Taking Study Guide

SECURITY IN A DANGEROUS WORLD

Focus Question: What kinds of threats to national and global security do nations face today?

As you read this section in your textbook, complete the chart below to compare threats to global security.

Threats to Security						
	Nuclear weapons are unsecured in Soviet Union.					
	Nuclear Weapons					

© Pearson Education, Inc., publishing as Pearson Prentice Hall. All rights reserved.

CHAPTER 19 SECTION 4 — Section Summary
SECURITY IN A DANGEROUS WORLD

Weapons of mass destruction (WMDs) include nuclear, biological, and chemical weapons. During the Cold War, the United States and Russia built up arsenals of nuclear weapons. To ensure that nuclear weapons did not **proliferate,** or spread rapidly, many nations signed the Nuclear Nonproliferation Treaty (NPT) in 1968. However, the treaty does not guarantee that nuclear weapons will not be used. Four nations have not signed the treaty, and other nations, such as Iran and North Korea, are suspected of buying and selling nuclear weapons even though they are treaty members. Stockpiles of nuclear weapons in the former Soviet Union are a special concern. This is because the Russian government has not had money to secure the weapons properly.

In the 2000s, terrorist groups and "rogue states" began to use WMDs for their own purposes. **Terrorism** is the use of violence, especially against civilians, to achieve political goals. Terrorist groups use headline-grabbing tactics to draw attention to their demands. Regional terrorist groups, such as the Irish Republican Army (IRA), operated for decades. They commit bombings, shootings, and kidnappings to force their governments to change policies. Increasingly, the Middle East has become a training ground and source for terrorism. Islamic fundamentalism motivates many of these groups. One powerful Islamic fundamentalist group is **al Qaeda,** whose leader is Osama bin Laden. Al Qaeda terrorists were responsible for the attacks on the United States on September 11, 2001.

Al Qaeda's attacks triggered a global reaction. Fighting terrorism became a central goal of both national and international policies. In 2001, Osama bin Laden and other al Qaeda leaders were living in **Afghanistan.** When Afghanistan's Islamic fundamentalist leaders, the **Taliban,** refused to surrender the terrorists, the United States attacked Afghanistan and overthrew them. Because President Bush believed that Saddam Hussein of Iraq was secretly producing WMDs, the United States also declared war on Iraq. <u>In addition, increased security at home became a priority.</u> As a result, the United States created a new Department of Homeland Security and instituted more rigorous security measures at airports and public buildings.

VOCABULARY STRATEGY

What does the word *priority* mean in the underlined sentence? Notice the sentence that follows it. What did the United States do because security was a *priority*? Use this context clue to help you understand the meaning of the word *priority*.

READING SKILL

Compare and Contrast Compare and contrast information about nuclear weapons before and after the Nuclear Nonproliferation Treaty.

_____

_____

_____

Review Questions

1. Why are nuclear weapons in the former Soviet Union a special concern?

_____

_____

2. Why did the United States declare war on Iraq?

_____

_____

© Pearson Education, Inc., publishing as Pearson Prentice Hall. All rights reserved.

CHAPTER
19
SECTION 5

Note Taking Study Guide

ADVANCES IN SCIENCE AND TECHNOLOGY

Focus Question: How have advances in science and technology shaped the modern world?

As you read this section in your textbook, complete the chart below to compare the impacts of modern science and technology.

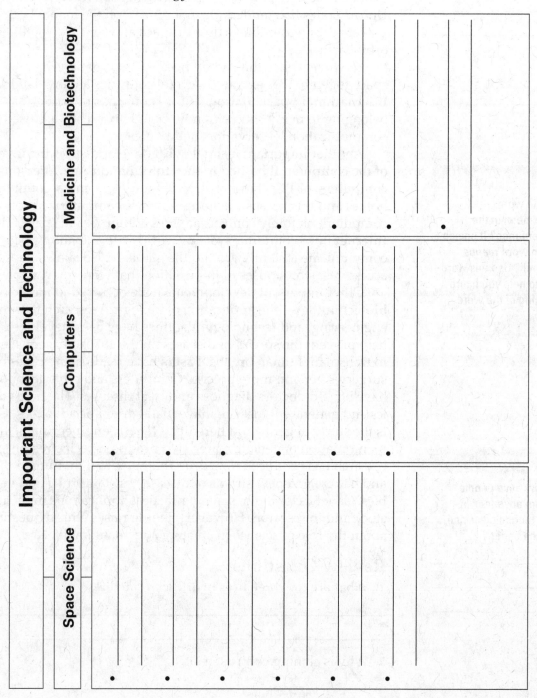

© Pearson Education, Inc., publishing as Pearson Prentice Hall. All rights reserved.

CHAPTER 19 SECTION 5

Section Summary

ADVANCES IN SCIENCE AND TECHNOLOGY

READING CHECK

What is biotechnology?

_____

_____

_____

VOCABULARY STRATEGY

What does the word *manipulation* mean in the underlined sentence? It comes from the Latin word *manus,* meaning "hand." Use this word-origins clue to help you figure out the meaning of the word *manipulation.*

READING SKILL

Compare How have people benefited from advances in science and technology since the space race began?

_____

_____

_____

Since 1945, scientific research and technological developments have transformed human existence. One example is the exploration of space. During the Cold War, the United States and the Soviet Union competed in a "space race." This began in 1957 when the Soviet Union launched *Sputnik,* the first **artificial satellite.** By 1969, the United States had landed the first human on the moon. Both super-powers explored military uses of space and sent spy satellites to orbit Earth.

However, since the end of the Cold War, nations have worked in space together. For example, several countries are involved in the **International Space Station (ISS).** Thousands of artificial satellites belonging to many countries now orbit Earth. They are used for communication, observation, and navigation.

Another important technological development is the invention of the computer. It has led to the "Information Age." **Personal computers**, or **PCs**, have replaced typewriters and account books in homes and businesses. Factories now use computerized robots, and computers remotely control satellites and probes in space. The **Internet** links computer systems worldwide and allows people to communicate instantly around the globe. It also allows people to access vast storehouses of information that were unavailable before.

Other important developments have occurred in medicine and **biotechnology**—the application of biological research to industry, engineering, and technology. Vaccines have been developed that help prevent the spread of diseases. In the 1970s, surgeons learned to transplant human organs. **Lasers** have made many types of surgery safer and more precise. Computers and other technologies have helped doctors diagnose and treat diseases. The fields of genet-ics and genetic engineering have made dramatic advances. **Genetics** is the study of genes and heredity. <u>**Genetic engineering** is the manipulation of genetic material to produce specific results.</u> Genetic research has produced new drug therapies to fight human diseases and has created new strains of disease-resistant fruits and vegeta-bles. Genetic cloning has many practical applications in raising live-stock and in research. However, cloning raises ethical questions about the role of science in creating and changing life.

Review Questions

1. What are the three uses of artificial satellites?

_____

_____

2. Why is cloning controversial?

_____

_____

© Pearson Education, Inc., publishing as Pearson Prentice Hall. All rights reserved.

Name_____ Class_____ Date_____

Concept Connector Study Guide

Belief Systems

Essential Question: What major belief systems have emerged over time?

A. Define *belief system.* _____
_____
_____

B. *Record information about the topics listed in the Cumulative Review or your answers to the questions in the Cumulative Review below. Use the Concept Connector Handbooks at the end of your textbook, as well as chapter information, to complete this worksheet.*

1. **Animism**
   The belief that the world is full of spirits and forces that reside in animals, objects, or dreams is known as animism. Animism has existed since prehistoric time. Cave paintings may be evidence that early peoples held animist beliefs. The paintings lie deep in caves, far from the everyday activities of the early people. They feature vivid images of deer, horses, and buffaloes. Some cave paintings show people, too. Scholars believe the paintings may have been created as part of animist religious rituals. Today animism is considered a primal-indigenous belief.

2. **Judaism**
   Scholars date the origins of Judaism to around 2000 B.C. The Jews of ancient history were known as Hebrews or Israelites. The beliefs of the Israelites differed in a significant way from other ancient people. The Israelites were monotheistic, believing in one God. The Israelites believed that God had made a covenant, or promise and binding agreement, with them. If the Jewish people obeyed God's commands, God would make Israel a great nation. Today, Judaism is considered a major world religion. Judaism influenced both Christianity and Islam.

3. **The Influence of Religion on Ancient Egyptian and Israelite Society**
   People in many early civilizations established belief systems that helped shape their societies. For example, religious beliefs about gods, values, and the afterlife affected daily life in ancient Egypt. Egypt's rulers, or pharaohs, were viewed as gods. Tremendous resources were used to prepare people for the afterlife. Israelites believed in an all-knowing, all-powerful God who was present everywhere. They believed that each event in their history reflected God's plan for them. As a result, they recorded events and laws in the Torah, their sacred text. Unlike ancient Egyptians, Jews saw their leaders as fully human and bound to obey God's law.

© Pearson Education, Inc., publishing as Pearson Prentice Hall. All rights reserved.

Concept Connector Study Guide

BELIEF SYSTEMS (continued)

4. Compare the Views of Ancient Egyptians and Ancient Indians

Different societies often have different beliefs about the results of a person's actions during his or her lifetime. The ancient Egyptians believed that after death a soul had to pass a test to win eternal life. Egyptians learned spells and formulas to use in the afterlife to prove their worthiness to the gods. Unlike ancient Egyptian beliefs, ancient Indians believed that their actions during life influenced what happened to them after they died. The beliefs of ancient Indians developed into concepts of dharma, karma, and reincarnation.

Dharma includes the religious and moral duties of an individual. *Karma* refers to all the actions of a person's life that affect his or her fate in the next life. *Reincarnation* is the rebirth of the soul in another bodily form.

5. Christianity

Christianity arose in the first century A.D. in Judea, which was part of the Roman empire at the time. It is based on the teachings of Jesus, a Jewish rabbi, or teacher. Jesus emphasized God's love and taught the need for justice, morality, and service to others. Christianity teaches that there is one God who sent Jesus to save humans. Jesus' disciples spread his message throughout the Roman empire after his death. Paul, an important early leader, traveled around the Mediterranean to set up churches. His letters form a large portion of the New Testament. The New Testament is part of the Bible, the sacred text of Christians, which also contains the Hebrew Bible. Although Christians were initially persecuted by Rome, Christianity eventually became the official religion of the Roman empire. Today Christianity is a major world religion with over 2 billion followers.

6. The Great Schism

Over time, Christianity developed differently in the eastern and western Roman empires. Christians in the east spoke Greek; Christians in the west spoke Latin. Theological differences caused controversies. During the Middle Ages, the two branches of Christianity drew farther apart. In the 700s, a dispute over the use of icons, or holy images, contributed to the problems. Finally, in 1054, the popes of the eastern and western churches excommunicated each other. The event is called the Great Schism. The eastern branch became known as the Eastern, or Orthodox, Church, while the western branch became known as the Roman Catholic Church. For centuries, the two churches treated each other as rivals rather than as branches of the same faith.

7. Muhammad and the Idea of Brotherhood

Islam has been an important force in history. The sayings of Muhammad, the founder of Islam, contributed to Islam's growth. For instance, Muhammad said, "Know ye that every Muslim is a brother to every other Muslim and that ye are now one brotherhood." Islam, which developed in the 600s, became a unifying force in the Arab world. Once Arabs united, they were able to conquer huge territories from the Persian empire to Spain. Islam emphasized the equality of all believers, and many conquered people were attracted to the message of Islam.

© Pearson Education, Inc., publishing as Pearson Prentice Hall. All rights reserved.

Concept Connector Study Guide

BELIEF SYSTEMS (continued)

8. **Shinto**

Shinto developed in Japan by the A.D. 500s. Shinto is the worship of the forces of nature. Early Japanese clans honored kami, or superior powers that were natural or divine. Shinto, meaning "the way of kami," became an important religion in Japan. Hundreds of Shinto shrines dot the Japanese countryside. These shrines are located in beautiful and natural surroundings, and may be dedicated to objects such as mountains, waterfalls, gnarled trees, or oddly shaped rocks.

9. **Impact of Missionaries** (Chapter 9, page 315)

_____

_____

_____

_____

_____

_____

_____

_____

© Pearson Education, Inc., publishing as Pearson Prentice Hall. All rights reserved.

Concept Connector Study Guide

BELIEF SYSTEMS *(continued)*

C. Sample Topics for Thematic Essays

Below are examples of thematic essay topics that might appear on a test. Prepare for the test by outlining an essay for each topic on a separate sheet of paper. Use the Concept Connector Handbooks at the end of your textbook, as well as chapter information, to outline your essays.

1. Describe the special covenant the Israelites believed that God made with Abraham and his descendants.

2. Discuss several major events or issues that encouraged the spread of Christianity.

3. Describe attitudes of Enlightenment thinkers, such as Voltaire, toward established religions and how church authorities responded.

4. Describe the role of religion in Otto von Bismarck's *Kulturkampf*. What were Bismarck's goals? What were the ultimate results of the *Kulturkampf*?

5. Discuss ways that churches and synagogues reacted to the changing social conditions of the Industrial Revolution.

6. Describe the beliefs of Methodism, founded by John Wesley in the mid-1700s, and its effects on industrial workers at the time.

7. Describe the influence of religion on the partition of India and Pakistan, and its role in the continuing conflicts between the two countries.

8. Discuss the role of the Islamist movement in removing the Shah of Iran in 1979 and how it has changed life there.

© Pearson Education, Inc., publishing as Pearson Prentice Hall. All rights reserved.

Concept Connector Study Guide

Conflict

Essential Question: What issues cause groups of people or countries to come into conflict?

A. Define *conflict.* _____
_____
_____

B. *Record information about the topics listed in the Cumulative Review or your answers to the questions in the Cumulative Review below. Use the Concept Connector Handbooks at the end of your textbook, as well as chapter information, to complete this worksheet.*

1. **The Persian Wars**
   Greek city-states developed different forms of government but shared a common culture and values. Greeks briefly put aside their differences to defend their freedom when the Persians threatened them. Ionian Greek city-states in Asia Minor became subjects of the Persian empire. In 499 B.C., Ionian Greeks rebelled against Persian rule, and the great city-state of Athens sent ships to help the Ionians. Then, in 490 B.C., Darius I of Persia sent his army to Greece to punish Athens. The large army landed near Marathon and was defeated by a much smaller Greek force. Ten years later, Xerxes, another Persian ruler, sent another force to conquer Greece. Finally, in 479 B.C., the Persian invasions ended when the Greeks defeated the Persians on land in Asia Minor.

2. **Compare the Persian Wars and the Punic Wars**
   Roman settlements spread throughout the Mediterranean, just as Greek city-states did around the Aegean. Both groups came into conflict with peoples across the sea. The Greeks fought the Persian Wars, in part to preserve Greek culture, when threatened by the Persians. As Rome grew in power, it came into conflict with Carthage, a great city-state in North Africa that ruled an empire stretching across the western Mediterranean. Between 264 B.C. and 146 B.C., Rome fought three wars against Carthage. These wars are called the Punic Wars. In the Second Punic War, the Carthaginian general Hannibal led his army, including war elephants, on an epic march from Spain over the Alps, to make a surprise attack on Rome. However, the Carthaginians were ultimately defeated and Rome was free to build an empire around the Mediterranean.

© Pearson Education, Inc., publishing as Pearson Prentice Hall. All rights reserved.

Concept Connector Study Guide
CONFLICT *(continued)*

3. Compare War Between Christians and Muslims in the 700s with the Crusades

The Crusades, which began in 1096, were not the first wars between Christians and Muslims. As the Muslim empire expanded west, it advanced into Europe. In the 700s, that advance was halted by Christian warriors at the Battle of Tours, in what is present-day France. After this, Muslim forces never again significantly threatened to take over Western Europe. Over 300 years later, invasions by Muslim Turks threatened the Byzantine empire and prevented Christian pilgrims from traveling to the Holy Land. Muslims and Christians fought for control of lands in the Middle East. These wars, called the Crusades, continued off and on for over 200 years. Religion, desire for wealth and land, and a yearning for adventure were just some of the factors that motivated European crusaders. Although the Crusades left a legacy of religious hatred, they also increased trade, the power of the pope, and the power of European monarchs.

4. Examples of French-British Conflict

As the French and British began to establish global empires in the 1600s and 1700s, they frequently came into conflict. This was not the first time that these two nations had opposed each other. An earlier example of French-British conflict occurred between France and England during the Hundred Years' War from 1337 to 1453. English rulers wanted to hold on to what had become the French lands of their Norman ancestors. England and France were also rivals for control of the English Channel, the waterway between their two countries. Each also wanted to control trade in the region.

5. Greek Wars Against the Persian Empire (Chapter 1, page 49)

_____
_____
_____
_____
_____
_____
_____

6. Roman-Carthaginian Wars (Chapter 1, page 49)

_____
_____
_____
_____
_____
_____
_____

© Pearson Education, Inc., publishing as Pearson Prentice Hall. All rights reserved.

Concept Connector Study Guide
CONFLICT *(continued)*

7. Compare the American Revolution with the Thirty Years' War
(Chapter 2, page 77)

_____

_____

_____

_____

_____

_____

_____

8. European Revolutionaries in 1830 and 1848 (Chapter 4, page 163)

_____

_____

_____

_____

_____

_____

_____

_____

9. Congress of Vienna and the Paris Peace Conference (Chapter 11, page 383)

_____

_____

_____

_____

_____

_____

_____

_____

© Pearson Education, Inc., publishing as Pearson Prentice Hall. All rights reserved.

Concept Connector Study Guide

CONFLICT *(continued)*

10. The Chinese Communists and the Guomindang (Chapter 12, page 415)

_____

_____

_____

_____

_____

_____

_____

11. World War II (Chapter 14, page 495)

_____

_____

_____

_____

_____

_____

_____

12. The Recent Conflict in Northern Ireland and Earlier Religious Conflicts
(Chapter 17, page 597)

_____

_____

_____

_____

_____

_____

_____

© Pearson Education, Inc., publishing as Pearson Prentice Hall. All rights reserved.

Concept Connector Study Guide
CONFLICT *(continued)*

C. Sample Topics for Thematic Essays

Below are examples of thematic essay topics that might appear on a test. Prepare for the test by outlining an essay for each topic on a separate sheet of paper. Use the Concept Connector Handbooks at the end of your textbook, as well as chapter information,, to outline your essays.

1. Describe the events of the Peloponnesian War, and discuss the outcome of this conflict.

2. Explain why nationalists in Europe fought against rulers during the revolutions of 1830 and 1848, and discuss the results of their struggles.

3. Describe the basic issues that led to the conflicts in the Balkans during the nineteenth and twentieth centuries and how the rest of the world has reacted to them.

4. Describe the issues that led to the partition of Africa by European powers in the late 1800s, and discuss how they served as the basis for conflicts between Africans and colonial powers between 1900 and 1975.

5. Compare and contrast the issues that sparked the Latin American wars of independence in the 1800s with those that created the movement for independence in Africa after World War II.

6. Describe some of the key features of the struggle between the Chinese Communists and the Guomindang (Nationalists) from the 1920s through the 1940s.

7. Analyze the issues that led to the breakup of the Soviet Union and the fall of communism in Eastern Europe in the 1980s and 1990s.

8. Describe and discuss the issues today that divide some Arabs and Arabs and Israelis in the Middle East.

© Pearson Education, Inc., publishing as Pearson Prentice Hall. All rights reserved.

Concept Connector Study Guide

Cooperation

Essential Question: In what ways have groups of people or countries cooperated over time?

A. Define *cooperation.* _____

_____

_____

B. *Record information about the topics listed in the Cumulative Review or your answers to the questions in the Cumulative Review below. Use the Concept Connector Handbooks at the end of your textbook, as well as chapter information, to complete this worksheet.*

1. **Iroquois League**
   In Northeast America, several Native American groups spoke the same language, and shared similar traditions. They are collectively known as the Iroquois. Typically, the Iroquois cleared land and built villages in the forests. While Iroquois women farmed, men hunted and fought wars against rival groups. In order to stop the constant wars, the Iroquois formed the Iroquois League in the late 1500s. The Iroquois League was an alliance of the Mohawk, Oneida, Onondaga, Cayuga, and Seneca. Nations that were members of the Iroquois League governed their own villages but met jointly in a council to address larger issues.

2. **Roads and Trade Routes**
   In different civilizations, road systems and trade routes have played important roles in connecting people. Some have connected people within a civilization, while others have connected people in different civilizations and across geographic regions. Roads and trade draw cultures together. Roads and trade also allow culture, language, and ideas to spread. For example, around 700 B.C., Phoenicians from the eastern Mediterranean set up colonies from North Africa to Sicily to Spain. Historians have called the Phoenicians "carriers of civilization" because they spread Middle Eastern civilization around the Mediterranean. Their alphabet was adapted by the Greeks—from this Greek alphabet came the alphabet we use today. Another example of the importance of roads and trade routes is the Silk Road, which began as a series of trade routes under the Han dynasty (202 B.C.–A.D. 220) in China and eventually linked China to the Fertile Crescent in the Middle East.

© Pearson Education, Inc., publishing as Pearson Prentice Hall. All rights reserved.

Concept Connector Study Guide

COOPERATION *(continued)*

3. **Development of Medieval Trade Routes; Glorious Revolution; American Revolution** (Chapter 2, page 77)

_____

_____

_____

_____

_____

_____

_____

_____

4. **Coalitions Against Napoleon** (Chapter 3, page 139)

_____

_____

_____

_____

_____

_____

_____

_____

5. **Tactics of Abolitionist Groups** (Chapter 8, page 281)

_____

_____

_____

_____

_____

_____

_____

_____

© Pearson Education, Inc., publishing as Pearson Prentice Hall. All rights reserved.

Concept Connector Study Guide

COOPERATION *(continued)*

6. League of Nations (Chapter 11, page 383)

_____

_____

_____

_____

_____

_____

_____

7. United Nations (Chapter 14, page 495)

_____

_____

_____

_____

_____

_____

_____

8. European Community (Chapter 15, page 545)

_____

_____

_____

_____

_____

_____

_____

9. NGOs (Nongovernmental Organizations) (Chapter 19, page 663)

_____

_____

_____

_____

_____

_____

_____

© Pearson Education, Inc., publishing as Pearson Prentice Hall. All rights reserved.

Concept Connector Study Guide
COOPERATION *(continued)*

C. Sample Topics for Thematic Essays

Below are examples of thematic essay topics that might appear on a test. Prepare for the test by outlining an essay for each topic on a separate sheet of paper. Use the Concept Connector Handbooks at the end of your textbook, as well as chapter information, to outline your essays.

1. Describe how Roman citizens cooperated in governing Rome during the Roman republic.

2. Explain how Parliament and William and Mary of Orange cooperated in ruling England.

3. Discuss how Enlightenment thinkers in France, England, and other European countries cooperated to refine their ideas and to spread them across Europe and beyond.

4. Describe the role of cooperation in the American Revolution. Discuss which groups and individuals cooperated, and the government that was created as a result.

5. Describe the new level of cooperation pledged by the members of the League of Nations after World War I, and explain why the organization could not prevent World War II.

6. Describe the uneasy cooperation among Allied leaders Roosevelt, Churchill, and Stalin during World War II.

7. Describe the cooperative goals of the European Community (Common Market) and the European Union, and how it has improved the economies of its members.

8. Select two challenges the world faces in the twenty-first century, and discuss what kinds of cooperation will be needed meet them. Consider economic, social, environmental, or security issues.

© Pearson Education, Inc., publishing as Pearson Prentice Hall. All rights reserved.

Concept Connector Study Guide

Cultural Diffusion

Essential Question: In what ways have migration and trade affected cultures?

A. Define *cultural diffusion.* _____
_____
_____

B. *Record information about the topics listed in the Cumulative Review or your answers to the questions in the Cumulative Review below. Use the Concept Connector Handbooks at the end of your textbook, as well as chapter information, to complete this worksheet.*

1. **Cultural Diffusion in Early Human History**
Cultural diffusion has long been a key source of change in society. Some of the changes that took place during the Old Stone Age, the New Stone Age, and the time of early civilizations were likely the result of cultural diffusion. Developments during these periods include the use of fire, the creation of stone tools, the painting of caves, the domestication of plants and animals, and the development of early civilizations. These technologies were not invented everywhere at the same time. Knowledge traveled slowly, perhaps taking thousands of years to spread across continents.

2. **Arabic Numerals**
The system of writing numbers that we use today was devised by Gupta mathematicians in India. The Guptas ruled from A.D. 320 to about 540. The system is commonly called Arabic; however, Hindu-Arabic is the more accurate term. Arab merchants and traders introduced the numerals as they traveled around the Mediterranean. The numerals may have been introduced in Europe via the Muslim empire in Spain. A European manuscript containing the numerals was written in Spain in 976. The superiority of the Hindu-Arabic numeral system is evident by its use nearly everywhere.

3. **Decimal System**
Indian mathematicians also originated the concept of zero and developed the decimal system of numbers based on ten digits that we still use today. Mathematicians in the Islamic world adapted it to include decimal fractions. It was introduced to the West when a text written by the Muslim mathematician al-Khwarizmi in the 800s was translated into Latin in the 1200s.

© Pearson Education, Inc., publishing as Pearson Prentice Hall. All rights reserved.

Concept Connector Study Guide
CULTURAL DIFFUSION (continued)

4. Hinduism

Unlike most major religions, Hinduism has no single founder. Instead, it grew out of the overlapping beliefs of diverse groups who settled in India. Aryans began arriving in India by 1500 B.C. They added the gods of the Indus civilization to their own. Later people brought other gods, beliefs, and practices. As a result, Hinduism became one of the world's most complex religions, with many gods and goddesses, and many forms of worship. It has been said that Hinduism accepts all forms of belief and worship, and does not eliminate any.

5. Buddhism

Buddhism developed in India around 600 B.C. Its founder, Siddhartha Gautama, became known as the Buddha. Buddhism and Hinduism have some similarities, including ideas about nonviolence and reincarnation. Unlike Hinduism, with its focus on priests and rituals, Buddhism urges each person to seek enlightenment through meditation. Missionaries and merchants spread Buddhism to many parts of Asia. By A.D. 500, Buddhism had spread from India into China, Tibet, Korea, and Japan. Buddhism slowly declined in India. However, Hinduism absorbed some Buddhist ideas and added Buddha as another Hindu god.

6. Evolution of the Alphabet

Even today, we can see examples of the important effects of cultural diffusion all around us. Indeed, the words on this page are the result of cultural diffusion. The alphabet we use today was developed by the Phoenicians. The Phoenician system used 22 symbols that stood for consonant sounds. The Phoenician alphabet was borrowed and modified by the Greeks. The Greeks added symbols for vowel sounds. That alphabet was then borrowed and adapted by the Romans. The alphabet was spread through trade and conquest, and because it was easier to use than other ancient writing systems, such as cuneiform or hieroglyphics.

7. The Spread of Roman Culture

Roman conquests and the empire (A.D. 27–A.D. 476) helped to spread Roman culture. That culture included language, literature, values, engineering, and laws. The Romans built roads to allow them easy access to all parts of the empire, and these roads allowed Roman culture to spread throughout Europe, North Africa, and the Middle East. The Romans developed laws to govern their large empire. Even after the empire fell, the Roman concept of law remained. Language, too, became a vehicle for spreading Roman culture. Romans wrote histories and epic poems that are read today. Latin remained the language of educated people and of the Roman Catholic Church for hundreds of years.

8. The Spread of Christianity and the Spread of Buddhism

The spread of religions depends on a variety of factors, including the appeal of the religion's message and political support. Both Buddhism and Christianity spread far and wide from their original locations. Buddhism developed in South Asia in the late sixth to fourth century B.C. Today there are 373 million followers all over the world. Christianity developed in the early first century A.D. in the Middle East. There are over 2 billion Christians today. Both religions used missionaries to spread their beliefs.

© Pearson Education, Inc., publishing as Pearson Prentice Hall. All rights reserved.

Concept Connector Study Guide
CULTURAL DIFFUSION (continued)

9. **The Roman and Byzantine Empires**

   Byzantine rulers thought of their empire as the successor to the Roman empire. Like the Romans before them, the Byzantines spread their culture across a wide expanse of Europe. Both empires diffused language and learning, religion, art and architecture, and political ideas. The Byzantine Church, known as the Eastern, or Orthodox, Church spread throughout Eastern Europe, the Balkans, and Russia. Byzantine scholars preserved the classic works of ancient Greece. As the Byzantine empire weakened in the 1400s, scholars left the Byzantine capital to teach in universities in the West. The work of these scholars contributed to the cultural flowering in Europe known as the Renaissance.

10. **The Spread of Islam**

   Islam began in the Middle East in the A.D. 600s. Islam's founder, Muhammad, created rules that governed and united Muslims, and brought peace. As his reputation grew, thousands of Arabs adopted Islam. Islam is both a religion and a way of life. After the death of Muhammad, Islam continued to spread as the Muslim empire grew. Conquered people were treated fairly; Islam's message emphasized equality; Arab trade networks developed; and Muslim empires developed in Spain, Persia, and India. All these factors contributed to the spread of Islam. Today, there are over one billion followers of Islam all over the world.

11. **The Spread of Ideas and Culture as a Result of Buddhist and Christian Missionaries**

   Missionaries share more than their religious beliefs. They also help to spread language, values, technology, and ideas about laws and government. In the 500s, Buddhist missionaries introduced Chinese writing and customs to Japan. A Buddhist form of architecture, known as the stupa, developed into the Japanese pagoda. In the 800s, Christians from the Eastern, or Orthodox, Church adapted the Greek alphabet so they could translate the Bible into the Slavic languages. This alphabet is still used in Russia, Ukraine, Serbia, and Bulgaria. Russians adopted other aspects of the missionaries' culture, including art, music, and architecture.

12. **The Renaissance and Islam**

   During the Middle Ages, many European peoples were cut off from one another as trade broke down and disease ravaged populations. With the Renaissance, renewed trade and increased curiosity about the world led to great cultural diffusion. For example, art techniques developed in Italy spread to northern Europe, and vice versa. Cultural diffusion also occurred as Islam spread between 750 and 1200. Muslim merchants introduced the Indian numerals we use today to the western world. Muslim advances in mathematics and medicine spread as books were translated into Latin. These books became the standard texts in European schools for hundreds of years.

© Pearson Education, Inc., publishing as Pearson Prentice Hall. All rights reserved.

Concept Connector Study Guide
CULTURAL DIFFUSION *(continued)*

13. **The Renaissance and the Tang and Song Dynasties**

    The European Renaissance ushered in a period of great cultural achievements that would eventually influence people far beyond Europe. The Tang and Song dynasties of China also saw important accomplishments. The Chinese achievements came earlier and in some cases paved the way for later European developments. For example, the Chinese invention of movable type foreshadowed the later European invention of the printing press. The Chinese developed a smallpox vaccine, invented a spinning wheel, and pioneered the use of arches in bridge building. Many of these developments traveled westward.

14. **Indian Influence on Southeast Asia**

    Indian culture influenced the cultures of Southeast Asia. Indian merchants and Hindu priests traveled throughout Southeast Asia, slowly spreading their culture. Later, Buddhist monks and scholars introduced their beliefs. Following the path of trade and religion came the influences of writing, law, government, art, architecture, and farming techniques. Southeast Asians visited India as pilgrims or students. As these contacts increased, Indian beliefs and ideas won widespread acceptance. The Khmer empire (800–1350) is one example of where this occurred. In the 1100s, a Khmer ruler built a temple complex in present-day Cambodia. Hundreds of carvings depict Hindu myths.

15. **The Growth of Christianity and the Growth of the Roman Empire**
    (Chapter 1, page 49)

    _____

    _____

    _____

    _____

    _____

    _____

    _____

16. **Influence of Ancient Civilizations on Enlightenment Thinkers**
    (Chapter 2, page 77)

    _____

    _____

    _____

    _____

    _____

    _____

    _____

© Pearson Education, Inc., publishing as Pearson Prentice Hall. All rights reserved.

Concept Connector Study Guide

CULTURAL DIFFUSION *(continued)*

C. Sample Topics for Thematic Essays

Below are examples of thematic essay topics that might appear on a test. Prepare for the test by outlining an essay for each topic on a separate sheet of paper. Use the Concept Connector Handbooks at the end of your textbook, as well as chapter information, to outline your essays.

1. Describe how Greco-Roman culture spread through the Roman empire during the *Pax Romana*.

2. Explain the role of cultural diffusion in the spread of Christianity. What factors encouraged Christianity's spread?

3. Describe how the migration to Ireland in the 1600s changed the political and economic structure of the country and the impact of the Great Hunger of the 1840s.

4. Describe how British rule led to cultural diffusion in India, and explain the attitude of Ram Mohun Roy toward Indian and Western culture.

5. Analyze the role of cultural diffusion in the modernization of Japan beginning in the 1850s.

6. How does migration and trade affect culture? Provide at least two examples from world history of the effects of migration and trade on cultural diffusion.

7. Discuss how increased trade and the demands of a global economy have changed people's lives in today's developing countries.

8. Describe at least two examples of cultural diffusion in the world today.

© Pearson Education, Inc., publishing as Pearson Prentice Hall. All rights reserved.

Concept Connector Study Guide

Democracy

Essential Question: How has the practice of democracy developed over time?

A. Define *democracy.* _____

_____

_____

B. *Record information about the topics listed in the Cumulative Review or your answers to the questions in the Cumulative Review below. Use the Concept Connector Handbooks at the end of your textbook, as well as chapter information, to complete this worksheet.*

1. **Roman Citizenship**
   Citizenship in Rome was important. In the Roman republic there was an official list of citizens. Citizenship conferred rights and responsibilities. For example, the Roman army was made up of citizen-soldiers. Roman citizens often made good soldiers because they were brought up to value loyalty, courage, and respect for authority. Rome developed one system of law that applied to citizens and another law system for non-citizens. Among the people Rome conquered, Rome gave the highly prized right of full citizenship to a few privileged groups, while other conquered people became partial citizens.

2. **Government by the People**
   In the Greek city-state of Athens, the idea of democracy first took root. Although many were excluded from the democratic process, citizens could gather and directly make important government decisions. In the Roman republic, as in the United States today, citizens were represented by a legislature. In 1215, English nobles forced King John to sign the Magna Carta. This document was another important step in the development of democracy. It asserted that nobles had certain rights. Over time, these rights were extended to all English citizens. In 1295, King Edward I summoned Parliament. For the first time representatives of the common people were part of Parliament. This Parliament later became known as the Model Parliament. It set up the framework for England's legislature.

3. **The Magna Carta and the English Bill of Rights**
   The Magna Carta of 1215 was a landmark in the development of democracy because it limited the power of the English monarch and protected some civil rights. The rights and protections ensured by the English Bill of Rights of 1689 also influenced the development of democracy. The Magna Carta granted rights mainly to nobles, gave the Great Council the right to tax, and protected citizens from arbitrary arrest. The Bill of Rights expanded these protections, placing additional limits on monarchs and bringing them under the law. It gave members of Parliament the right of free speech and the power to deny funds to the monarch. It also forbade cruel and unusual punishment of any citizen.

© Pearson Education, Inc., publishing as Pearson Prentice Hall. All rights reserved.

Concept Connector Study Guide
DEMOCRACY *(continued)*

4. The Petition of Right (Chapter 1, page 49)

_____

_____

_____

_____

_____

_____

5. Democracy in England and Ancient Greece (Chapter 1, page 49)

_____

_____

_____

_____

_____

_____

_____

6. The American Declaration of Independence (Chapter 2, page 77)

_____

_____

_____

_____

_____

_____

_____

7. The Declaration of the Rights of Man and the Citizen and the American Declaration of Independence (Chapter 3, page 139)

_____

_____

_____

_____

_____

_____

_____

© Pearson Education, Inc., publishing as Pearson Prentice Hall. All rights reserved.

Concept Connector Study Guide
DEMOCRACY (continued)

8. The American Revolution and Revolutions in Latin America
(Chapter 4, page 163)

_____

_____

_____

_____

_____

_____

_____

9. John Locke and the Expansion of Suffrage (Chapter 8, page 281)

_____

_____

_____

_____

_____

_____

_____

10. The Curtailment of Citizen's Rights (Chapter 14, page 495)

_____

_____

_____

_____

_____

_____

_____

© Pearson Education, Inc., publishing as Pearson Prentice Hall. All rights reserved.

Concept Connector Study Guide
DEMOCRACY *(continued)*

C. Sample Topics for Thematic Essays

Below are examples of thematic essay topics that might appear on a test. Prepare for the test by outlining an essay for each topic on a separate sheet of paper. Use the Concept Connector Handbooks at the end of your textbook, as well as chapter information, to outline your essays.

1. What do you think were the three most important steps in the development of democracy? Explain your choices.

2. How were the American and French Revolutions related?

3. Compare the beliefs of at least three cultures throughout history regarding power, authority, governance, and law.

4. How would you define citizenship, and how have different societies viewed the rights and responsibilities of citizenship?

5. How are contemporary democratic governments rooted in Enlightenment ideals?

6. What impacts did Greece and Rome have on the development of later political systems?

7. What forces led to the nineteenth-century failure of democracy in Latin America and Russia?

8. What role does democracy play in Latin America today?

© Pearson Education, Inc., publishing as Pearson Prentice Hall. All rights reserved.

Name_____ Class_____ Date_____

Concept Connector Study Guide

Dictatorship

Essential Question: How have dictators assumed and maintained power?

A. Define *dictatorship.* _____

_____

_____

B. *Record information about the topics listed in the Cumulative Review or your answers to the questions in the Cumulative Review below. Use the Concept Connector Handbooks at the end of your textbook, as well as chapter information, to complete this worksheet.*

1. Julius Caesar (Chapter 1, page 49)

_____

_____

_____

_____

_____

2. Mussolini and Hitler (Chapter 13, page 455)

_____

_____

_____

_____

3. Stalin and Other Russian Leaders (Chapter 13, page 455)

_____

_____

_____

_____

_____

© Pearson Education, Inc., publishing as Pearson Prentice Hall. All rights reserved.

Concept Connector Study Guide
DICTATORSHIP *(continued)*

4. Communist Dictators and Other Dictators (Chapter 15, page 545)

_____

_____

_____

_____

_____

_____

_____

5. Mobutu Sese Seko (Chapter 16, page 575)

_____

_____

_____

_____

_____

_____

_____

6. Saddam Hussein (Chapter 17, page 597)

_____

_____

_____

_____

_____

_____

7. The Rise of Latin American Dictators (Chapter 18, page 627)

_____

_____

_____

_____

_____

_____

_____

© Pearson Education, Inc., publishing as Pearson Prentice Hall. All rights reserved.

Concept Connector Study Guide

DICTATORSHIP *(continued)*

C. Sample Topics for Thematic Essays

Below are examples of thematic essay topics that might appear on a test. Prepare for the test by outlining an essay for each topic on a separate sheet of paper. Use the Concept Connector Handbooks at the end of your textbook, as well as chapter information, to outline your essays.

1. Compare and contrast the ways in which dictators gained control and the powers they had during the Roman republic and the Roman empire.

2. Discuss why many French people supported Napoleon, even though he was essentially a dictator.

3. Describe the conditions in Mexico that led to the revolution in 1910 against the dictator General Porfirio Díaz.

4. Describe the conditions in Italy that led to Mussolini's rise to power after World War I, and the ideas and methods that kept him in power until Italy's defeat in World War II.

5. Describe Hitler's belief in a "master race," and how he used it to gain power and promote war.

6. Compare and contrast the ideas of fascism and communism and the ways in which adherents gained and maintained power in Europe and Russia before World War II.

7. Compare Fulgencio Batista and Fidel Castro. What are the similarities and differences in how they came to power and how they ruled?

8. Describe the dictatorship in China since Mao Zedong died in 1976. What has been the country's approach to economic and political freedom in this period?

© Pearson Education, Inc., publishing as Pearson Prentice Hall. All rights reserved.

Concept Connector Study Guide

Economic Systems

Essential Question: What types of economic systems have societies used to produce and distribute goods and services?

A. Define *economic system*. _____

_____

_____

B. *Record information about the topics listed in the Cumulative Review or your answers to the questions in the Cumulative Review below. Use the Concept Connector Handbooks at the end of your textbook, as well as chapter information, to complete this worksheet.*

1. **The Expansion of Towns in Medieval Europe**
    Before the expansion of towns, the medieval economy was based on the manor. Manors were self-sufficient estates owned by lords that produced nearly everything that was needed. Peasants were required to work for the lord in return for his protection. During the Middle Ages, towns expanded. Trade revived, stimulating new ways of doing business. Groups of merchants formed partnerships. A new middle class, made up of merchants, traders, and artisans, came into being. Towns were very different from manors. Townspeople had no lord, could move about freely, and had different economic opportunities. Nobles resented the fact that they had no control over towns. The Church was concerned that the emphasis on trade and money was immoral. The growth of towns eventually reshaped medieval society. Peasants preferred to sell their produce to townspeople and pay rent to the lord in cash rather than labor. By 1300, most peasants in Western Europe rented their land or were hired laborers.

2. **Mercantilism and Manorialism**
    In the 1700s, European nations adopted the economic policy of mercantilism in order to gain wealth and build empires. Mercantilists believed that a nation's wealth was measured in its supply of gold and silver. Mercantilism depended heavily on the establishment of overseas colonies. Colonies provided resources and materials for the parent country. Colonists were required by laws to trade exclusively with the parent country. Manorialism was the economic system of the Middle Ages. A manor was a lord's estate, which included one or more villages and the surrounding lands. Most peasants on a manor were serfs bound to the land. A manor produced everything needed by the people who lived and worked on the manor. Much as mercantilism existed for the benefit of the parent country, the manor existed for the benefit of the lord.

© Pearson Education, Inc., publishing as Pearson Prentice Hall. All rights reserved.

Concept Connector Study Guide

ECONOMIC SYSTEMS *(continued)*

3. Market Economy (Chapter 5, page 191)

_____

_____

_____

_____

_____

_____

4. Centrally Planned Economy (Chapter 5, page 191)

_____

_____

_____

_____

_____

_____

_____

5. Mixed Economy (Chapter 5, page 191)

_____

_____

_____

_____

_____

_____

_____

6. Compare Socialism with Mercantilism (Chapter 5, page 191)

_____

_____

_____

_____

_____

_____

_____

© Pearson Education, Inc., publishing as Pearson Prentice Hall. All rights reserved.

Concept Connector Study Guide

ECONOMIC SYSTEMS *(continued)*

7. **The Commercial Revolution During the Middle Ages and the Industrial Revolution** (Chapter 6, page 223)

_____

_____

_____

_____

_____

_____

_____

8. **Command Economies in Developing Countries and in Russia** (Chapter 18, page 627)

_____

_____

_____

_____

_____

_____

_____

9. **Economic Systems in the Twentieth Century** (Chapter 19, page 641)

_____

_____

_____

_____

_____

_____

_____

© Pearson Education, Inc., publishing as Pearson Prentice Hall. All rights reserved.

Concept Connector Study Guide
ECONOMIC SYSTEMS (continued)

C. Sample Topics for Thematic Essays

Below are examples of thematic essay topics that might appear on a test. Prepare for the test by outlining an essay for each topic on a separate sheet of paper. Use the Concept Connector Handbooks at the end of your textbook, as well as chapter information, to outline your essays.

1. Discuss the economic system used by the British East India Company and the British government in India during the 1800s and how this system affected the economy in India.

2. Describe the "laissez-faire" approach to economics, and explain how the writings of Adam Smith supported this approach.

3. Describe the classes Karl Marx believed had struggled against one another throughout history, and discuss why Marxism lost much of its appeal as time passed.

4. Compare the economic system in Latin America during colonial times with the economic system after independence.

5. Contrast socialism with capitalism, and discuss the benefits early socialist reformers predicted would occur in the event that socialism replaced capitalism.

6. Discuss the role British mercantilism played in sparking the American Revolution.

7. Describe the economic changes in Eastern Europe after the fall of the Soviet Union and the challenges facing countries as they adapted from one economic system to another.

8. Contrast the Great Leap Forward of Mao Zedong in 1958 with the Four Modernizations of Deng Xiaoping in the 1980s, and discuss their results.

© Pearson Education, Inc., publishing as Pearson Prentice Hall. All rights reserved.

Concept Connector Study Guide

Empires

Essential Question: What factors allow empires to rise and what factors cause them to fall?

A. Define *empire.* _____

_____

_____

B. *Record information about the topics listed in the Cumulative Review or your answers to the questions in the Cumulative Review below. Use the Concept Connector Handbooks at the end of your textbook, as well as chapter information, to complete this worksheet.*

1. **Characteristics of Successful Rulers**

   To maintain control over a vast empire, it was vital that a ruler be well respected. Many characteristics or abilities make a successful ruler. These include spiritual leadership, law-giving, just punishment for crime, military power, and treatment of subjects. For example, about 1790 B.C., Hammurabi, king of Babylon, brought much of Mesopotamia under the control of his empire. Hammurabi is famous for publishing a set of laws known as Hammurabi's Code. This law code established civil law and defined crime and punishments. Hammurabi also improved the irrigation system, organized a well-trained army, and ordered repairs to temples. To encourage religious unity, he encouraged the worship of a particular Babylonian god.

2. **Empire-Building in India, China, Egypt, and the Middle East**

   Eventually empires weaken, and power changes hands. In some cases, the civilization continues. The history of ancient Egypt illustrates this. Scholars have divided Egypt's history into three main periods: the Old Kingdom (2575 B.C.–2130 B.C.), the Middle Kingdom (1938 B.C.–1630 B.C.), and the New Kingdom (1539 B.C.–1075 B.C.). Although power passed from one dynasty to another, Egypt remained united and the civilization continued. In China, various dynasties ruled from 1766 B.C. to A.D. 1911. Even as dynasties changed hands, China generally remained unified. In ancient India, however, the Maurya dynasty ruled, beginning in 321 B.C. Then in 185 B.C., battles for power destroyed the unity of the empire. It was not until 500 years later that a new empire, the Gupta, re-unified India. In the ancient Middle East, power passed from the Babylonians to the Assyrians, back to the Babylonians again, and then to the Persians. The culture changed under each ruling group.

© Pearson Education, Inc., publishing as Pearson Prentice Hall. All rights reserved.

Concept Connector Study Guide

EMPIRES (continued)

3. Methods of Control in the Roman Empire and Han Dynasty

The Roman empire (A.D. 27–A.D. 476) and the Han dynasty (202 B.C.–A.D. 220) in China each exerted control over a wide area and a variety of people. Roman legions maintained and protected roads, and Roman fleets chased pirates from the seas. Trade flowed freely to and from distant lands. Egyptian farmers supplied grain. Roman soldiers swiftly put down revolts. Roman officials provided spectacular entertainment for the public. Similarly, Han rulers improved roads and canals. They set up places to store grain so they could buy grain at low prices and sell it when grain was scarce. Han soldiers drove nomadic peoples out of the empire. Under the Han, trade routes to the West were opened. Both governments relied on a well-established bureaucracy to handle the details of governing a large empire.

4. Aztec and Inca

The Aztec (A.D. 1325–A.D. 1521) and the Inca (A.D. 1438–A.D. 1535) were two impressive civilizations of the Americas. Both civilizations could be described as empires. Through a combination of fierce conquests and shrewd alliances, the Aztec spread their rule across most of Mexico. The Aztec empire had a single ruler. A council of nobles, priests, and military leaders elected the emperor, whose primary function was to lead in war. Nobles served as officials, judges, and governors of conquered provinces. The Inca similarly used conquest and alliances to subdue neighboring groups. They used military and diplomatic skills to create their empire and established a chain of command that reached down to the family level. The Inca also imposed their language on conquered peoples. They created a network of roads across the empire, all connected to the capital. The roads aided communication. They also made it possible for the Inca to send armies to every corner of their empire.

5. Was Charlemagne Really King of the Romans?

The Roman empire ceased to exist in the West in A.D. 476. Germanic tribes, including the Goths, Vandals, Saxons and Franks, had conquered, or went on to conquer, parts of it. Between 400 and 700, they carved Western Europe into small kingdoms. In 768, Charlemagne became king of the Franks. He briefly united Western Europe when he built an empire reaching across what is now France, Germany, and part of Italy. In 800, Pope Leo III crowned Charlemagne the emperor of the Romans. By doing so, he proclaimed that Charlemagne was the successor to the Roman emperors.

6. The Roman Empire and the Holy Roman Empire

The name of the Holy Roman Empire was supposed to make people think of the greatness and power of the ancient Roman empire. There were, however, significant differences between the two empires. The Roman empire lasted about 450 years. Charlemagne's empire ended with his death. However, just as Charlemagne looked to the Roman empire as an example of greatness and power, later medieval leaders considered Charlemagne's rule to be their model.

© Pearson Education, Inc., publishing as Pearson Prentice Hall. All rights reserved.

Concept Connector Study Guide
EMPIRES *(continued)*

7. The Byzantine Empire

The Byzantine empire (330–1453) was a powerful and influential empire. As the cities of the western Roman empire crumbled, the Byzantine empire, with its capital at Constantinople, remained secure and prospered. The Byzantine empire was the source of several important developments, such as Justinian's Code and the spread of Christianity in Eastern Europe and Russia. For centuries, the Byzantine empire withstood attacks by Persians, Slavs, Vikings, Mongols, and Turks. The empire served as a buffer for Western Europe, preventing the spread of Muslim conquest. The Fourth Crusade in 1204 severely weakened the empire. In 1453, Constantinople fell to the Turks.

8. The Abbasid Empire

The Abbasid dynasty began in 750 when a Muslim leader named Abu al-Abbas captured Damascus and defeated the Umayyads. The Abbasids tried to create an empire based on the equality of all Muslims. The new rulers halted large military conquests, ending the dominance of the Arab military class. Discrimination against non-Arab Muslims largely ended. Under the early Abbasids, Muslim civilization flourished. The Abbasids moved the capital to Baghdad. Poets, scholars, and philosophers came there from all over the Muslim world. Baghdad exceeded Constantinople in size and wealth. However, around 850 the empire began to fragment.

9. The Mughal Empire

The Mughal dynasty (1526–1857) was the second Muslim dynasty to rule the Indian subcontinent. The Mughal dynasty was set up by Babur, who claimed descent from the Mongol ruler Genghis Khan. The chief builder of the Mughal empire was Babur's grandson Akbar. During his long reign, from 1556 to 1605, he created a strong central government, earning the title Akbar the Great. He modernized the army, encouraged international trade, standardized weights and measures, and introduced land reforms. Although a Muslim, he won the support of his Hindu subjects through his policy of toleration. He opened government jobs to Hindus of all castes.

10. Suleiman the Magnificent

The Ottomans were a Turkish-speaking people whose Muslim empire ruled the Middle East and parts of Eastern Europe. In 1453, the Ottomans captured Constantinople, renamed it Istanbul, and ruled from there for the next 200 years. The Ottoman empire enjoyed a golden age under Suleiman, who ruled from 1520 to 1566. Europeans called him Suleiman the Magnificent. A brilliant general, Suleiman modernized the army and conquered many new lands. He extended Ottoman rule eastward into the Middle East, and also into Central Asia. In 1529, his armies besieged the Austrian city of Vienna, causing great fear in Western Europe. The Ottomans ruled the largest, most powerful empire in both Europe and the Middle East for centuries.

© Pearson Education, Inc., publishing as Pearson Prentice Hall. All rights reserved.

Concept Connector Study Guide

EMPIRES (continued)

11. The Mongol Empire

The Mongols were a nomadic people who grazed their horses and sheep on the steppes of Central Asia. In about 1200, a Mongol chieftain united rival Mongol clans. The chieftain took the name Genghis Khan, meaning "Universal Ruler." Under Genghis Khan, and his grandson Kublai Khan, the Mongols conquered an empire that spread from Europe in the west to China in the east. Under the protection of the Mongols, who controlled the great Silk Road, trade flourished across Eurasia. Cultural exchanges increased as foods, tools, inventions, and ideas spread along the protected trade routes.

12. The Ming Empire

With the death of Kublai Khan in 1294, Mongol rule in China weakened. In 1368, a new dynasty, called the Ming, took over. Early Ming rulers sought to reassert Chinese greatness after years of Mongol rule. The Ming restored the civil service system. The economy grew as new agricultural methods produced more crops. Ming China saw a revival of the arts and literature. Ming artists developed their own styles of landscape painting and created brilliant blue-and-white porcelain. People enjoyed new forms of literature, such as novels and detective stories. The Ming sent Chinese fleets to explore distant lands and to show off the glory of the Ming empire. The Ming dynasty ended in 1644.

13. The Roman Empire and the Tang Dynasty

The Roman empire and the Tang dynasty (A.D. 618–A.D. 907) in China each established a system of government to rule over their lands. Both empires had law codes and a well-developed bureaucracy or civil service. Both empires benefited from competent emperors. Rulers in both empires took steps to strengthen the central government and increase revenues through taxes. In both empires, social and economic problems, as well as invasions, weakened the governments. Both empires collapsed after a period of decline.

14. The Qing and the Yuan Dynasties

Twice in China's history foreign dynasties ruled the region. The first was the Yuan dynasty, in the late 1200s, established by the Mongols. Kublai Khan, the first Yuan leader, tried to prevent Mongols from being absorbed into Chinese civilization. He reserved the highest government jobs for Mongols and decreed that only Mongols could serve in the military. Under the Yuan, contact between Europe and Asia continued. The pope sent priests to the capital and Chinese products were sent West. In the 1600s, invaders from Manchuria, known as Manchus, toppled the Ming dynasty. The Manchus set up a dynasty known as the Qing, which ruled China until 1911. Unlike the Yuan, the Qing left local government in the hands of the Chinese. For each high government position, the Qing chose two people, one Manchu and one Chinese. The Manchus adopted the Confucian system of government, and this won them the support of important Chinese scholar-officials. Unlike the Yuan, the Qing restricted contact with Europeans.

© Pearson Education, Inc., publishing as Pearson Prentice Hall. All rights reserved.

Concept Connector Study Guide

EMPIRES *(continued)*

15. **The Roman Empire and the Spanish Empire in the Americas**
Both the Romans and the Spanish established empires over a wide area. There were similarities and differences between the two empires. Rome allowed local peoples to retain their own religions and cultures as long as they did not come into conflict with Roman rule. The Spanish, on the other hand, tried to convert their subjects to Christianity and to "civilize" them according to European ways. Rome and Spain gave some room for local people to govern at local levels, though each retained centralized control in the parent country. Superior technology gave both empires advantages over other societies. Disease, which aided Spain in establishing an empire, was not a factor for Rome.

16. **The Roman Empire** (Chapter 1, page 49)

_____

_____

_____

_____

_____

_____

17. **North American Colonies and Latin American Colonies** (Chapter 4, page 163)

_____

_____

_____

_____

_____

_____

18. **The Second Reich and the Holy Roman Empire** (Chapter 7, page 253)

_____

_____

_____

_____

_____

_____

© Pearson Education, Inc., publishing as Pearson Prentice Hall. All rights reserved.

Concept Connector Study Guide
EMPIRES *(continued)*

19. The Spanish Empire of the 1500s and the British Empire of the late 1800s
(Chapter 9, page 315)

_____

_____

_____

_____

_____

_____

20. Arguments Against Imperialism (Chapter 9, page 315)

_____

_____

_____

_____

_____

_____

21. The Soviet Union and Other Empires (Chapter 15, page 545)

_____

_____

_____

_____

_____

_____

22. Chechnya and Earlier Efforts to Break Away from an Empire
(Chapter 17, page 597)

_____

_____

_____

_____

_____

_____

© Pearson Education, Inc., publishing as Pearson Prentice Hall. All rights reserved.

Concept Connector Study Guide
EMPIRES *(continued)*

C. Sample Topics for Thematic Essays

Below are examples of thematic essay topics that might appear on a test. Prepare for the test by outlining an essay for each topic on a separate sheet of paper. Use the Concept Connector Handbooks at the end of your textbook, as well as chapter information, to outline your essays.

1. Describe Britain's attitudes toward its colonies during the 1700s and the reasons why the Americans were able to break away from the British empire.

2. Discuss reasons why Napoleon was able to build an empire in the early 1800s, and the reasons for its fall.

3. Describe the results of the Congress of Vienna in 1815 and the forces that challenged the old empires during the next 30 years.

4. Describe the Hapsburg empire in the early 1800s and the conflicts that made the Balkans a "powder keg" before World War I.

5. Describe the reasons why the Ottoman empire was in decline by the 1700s, and explain why the Europeans were able to take control of much of the Ottoman empire in the 1800s.

6. Discuss why Great Britain was able to expand its areas of control in India after 1765 and the policies that set the stage for later independence movements.

7. Describe reasons why Western powers were able to gain control over much of the world between 1870 and the beginning of World War I.

8. Discuss reasons for the fall of communism and the breakup of the Soviet Union in the 1980s.

© Pearson Education, Inc., publishing as Pearson Prentice Hall. All rights reserved.

Concept Connector Study Guide

Genocide

Essential Question: What factors have led groups of people or governments to commit genocide?

A. Define *genocide.* _____

_____

_____

B. *Record information about the topics listed in the Cumulative Review or your answers to the questions in the Cumulative Review below. Use the Concept Connector Handbooks at the end of your textbook, as well as chapter information, to complete this worksheet.*

1. **Native Americans**
   Beginning in 1492, the arrival of Europeans in the Americas led to the deaths of millions of Native Americans. Europeans unknowingly carried diseases for which native populations had no immunity. In some cases, Native American populations declined by as much as 90 percent. With the use of superior weapons and horses, and the effects of disease, Europeans were able to conquer native populations. Under the encomienda system, Spanish conquerors forced Native Americans to work under the most brutal conditions. Those who resisted were hunted down and killed.

2. **Indigenous People in North America, Australia, and New Zealand**
   (Chapter 10, page 345)

   _____

   _____

   _____

   _____

   _____

   _____

   _____

   _____

© Pearson Education, Inc., publishing as Pearson Prentice Hall. All rights reserved.

Name_____ Class_____ Date_____

Concept Connector Study Guide
GENOCIDE *(continued)*

3. The Holocaust and the Armenian Genocide (Chapter 14, page 495)

_____

_____

_____

_____

_____

_____

_____

_____

4. Genocide in Cambodia Compared with Earlier Genocides
  (Chapter 15, page 545)

_____

_____

_____

_____

_____

_____

_____

_____

_____

5. Genocide in Rwanda Compared with Earlier Genocides (Chapter 17, page 597)

_____

_____

_____

_____

_____

_____

_____

_____

_____

© Pearson Education, Inc., publishing as Pearson Prentice Hall. All rights reserved.

Concept Connector Study Guide
GENOCIDE *(continued)*

C. Sample Topics for Thematic Essays

Below are examples of thematic essay topics that might appear on a test. Prepare for the test by outlining an essay for each topic on a separate sheet of paper. Use the Concept Connector Handbooks at the end of your textbook, as well as chapter information, to outline your essays.

1. Discuss reasons why the Romans persecuted early Christians and how Roman attitudes changed during the 300s A.D.

2. Describe the differences between Armenians and the Ottoman Turks in the late 1800s, and discuss the factors that led to the genocide of the early 1900s.

3. Discuss Nazi attitudes towards Jews and other ethnic groups and how these views were used to justify the events of the Holocaust.

4. Describe the genocide in Cambodia under the Khmer Rouge. How does the genocide in Cambodia differ from other genocides, such as the Holocaust?

5. Discuss the violence in Latin America that occurred from the 1960s into the 1990s, including the tactics used by Guatemala's military against the indigenous population. Is this an example of genocide?

6. Describe ethnic and religious differences among groups in the former Yugoslavia and how they led to attempted genocide in Kosovo in the 1990s.

7. Discuss the reasons why genocide occurred in Rwanda in the 1990s and the international response.

8. Discuss the ethnic conflict in Sudan's western region of Darfur. Why has this conflict raised fears of a new genocide?

© Pearson Education, Inc., publishing as Pearson Prentice Hall. All rights reserved.

Concept Connector Study Guide

Geography's Impact

Essential Question: How have geographic factors affected the course of history?

A. Define *geography*. _____

_____

_____

B. *Record information about the topics listed in the Cumulative Review or your answers to the questions in the Cumulative Review below. Use the Concept Connector Handbooks at the end of your textbook, as well as chapter information, to complete this worksheet.*

1. **Rivers and the Rise of Civilization**
   The earliest civilizations to develop were situated on major rivers. Rivers provided important resources such as a regular water supply and a means of transportation. The animals that flocked to rivers were a source of food. Most important, conditions in river valleys favored farming. Floodwaters spread silt across the valleys, renewing the soil and keeping it fertile. Examples of civilizations that developed near a major river are Sumer, between the Tigris and Euphrates; the Indus River valley civilization; and Egypt on the Nile.

2. **The Tigris and Euphrates Rivers**
   The Tigris and Euphrates rivers played an important role in the development of the world's first civilization around 3300 B.C. in a region called Sumer. Sumer was located between these two rivers. The rivers lie within the Fertile Crescent, a region in the Middle East. The rivers often flooded, destroying farmland, so early villagers learned to work together to control flooding. In the dry season, people worked together to channel water to the fields. Temple priests or officials provided leadership for these large projects. Within a few hundred years, 12 city-states were located in the region.

3. **The Aegean and Mediterranean Seas**
   The civilizations of the Minoans, Mycenaeans, and ancient Greeks were greatly influenced by the Aegean and Mediterranean seas. The Minoans (1600 B.C.–1400 B.C.) and Mycenaeans (1400 B.C.–1200 B.C.) were sea traders. Through trade, both groups came into contact with Egypt and Mesopotamia. From these contacts, they acquired ideas about writing and architecture that they adapted to their own cultures. Mountains divided Greek city-states from one another. For the Greeks, the seas provided a vital link to the world outside. The Greeks became skilled sailors and carried cargoes throughout the eastern Mediterranean and, through trade, also acquired new ideas. By 750 B.C., population growth forced many Greeks to expand overseas. Greek colonies developed around the Mediterranean. Wherever they traveled, Greek settlers carried their ideas and culture.

© Pearson Education, Inc., publishing as Pearson Prentice Hall. All rights reserved.

Concept Connector Study Guide
GEOGRAPHY'S IMPACT (continued)

4. Geographic Environments of Developing Civilizations

Rivers, seas, mountains, valleys, and rain forests have been very important to civilizations. Geographic features can encourage or discourage trade, lead to cultural diffusion and cooperation, and provide protection from attack. In Mesoamerica, the Aztec built their capital on a swampy island in Lake Texcoco. To increase farmland, the Aztec built floating gardens of earth and reeds. They created canals for transportation and linked the city to the mainland with wide stone causeways. In South Asia, the Himalayas and Hindu Kush mountains protected the developing civilizations of Harappa and Mohenjo-Daro from invaders. Melting snow from the mountains flowed into the Indus and Brahmaputra rivers, making agriculture possible.

5. The Ocean's Influence on the Vikings

The Vikings made their home in Scandinavia, in the region that now includes Norway, Sweden, and Denmark. They were expert sailors. In the 700s, they sailed down the coasts and rivers of Europe, looting and burning communities. They were also traders and explorers, setting up trade routes as far as the Mediterranean. Vikings settled across the ocean in England, Ireland, France, and parts of Russia.

6. The Importance of Rivers to Early Cultures

The rivers of Russia and Eastern Europe provided highways for migration, trade, and ideas. Russia's network of rivers, running north to south, linked early Russians to the advanced Byzantine world in the south. Vikings used the rivers to trade with Constantinople, the Byzantine capital. It was from a Viking tribe called the Rus that Russia got its name. The rivers of Eastern Europe also flow north and south. Consequently, the cultures of Eastern Europe felt the influence of Russia and the Byzantine empire. When Constantinople fell to the Ottoman Turks in 1453, Eastern European cultures were influenced by the Muslims.

7. Geography and Cultural Development in Eastern Europe and Africa

In Eastern Europe, geographic features such as rivers allowed easy movement of people, goods, and ideas. In Africa, geographic features were often barriers to movement. The Sahara, a vast desert, hindered trade until the introduction of the camel from Asia as a form of transportation. The interior of Africa is a high plateau. Rivers with waterfalls were barriers to trade and movement. On the other hand, the Great Rift Valley served as an interior passageway and the Mediterranean and Red seas provided trade routes to regions in southeast Asia and present-day Europe. Between 800 and 1600, valuable resources such as gold, salt, iron, and copper brought great wealth to African kingdoms and trading states.

8. The Impact of Geography in Japan and Mesopotamia

Mesopotamian civilization developed in the Fertile Crescent between the Tigris and Euphrates rivers. There were very few natural barriers. Nomadic peoples or ambitious warriors descended on the rich cities of the Fertile Crescent. The region was also a crossroads for the mingling of beliefs and ideas. On the other hand, geography set Japan apart. Japan is made up of a series of islands. Most of the land was too mountainous to farm. The seas protected and isolated Japan. They also offered plentiful food resources, and the Japanese developed a thriving fishing industry. Japan's isolation helped it develop and maintain a distinct culture.

© Pearson Education, Inc., publishing as Pearson Prentice Hall. All rights reserved.

Concept Connector Study Guide

GEOGRAPHY'S IMPACT *(continued)*

9. **Location and the Relationship Between Latin America and the United States, 1800–1914** (Chapter 10, page 345)

_____

_____

_____

_____

_____

_____

_____

_____

10. **The Effect of Oil on the History of Saudi Arabia and the United States** (Chapter 16, page 575)

_____

_____

_____

_____

_____

_____

_____

_____

_____

© Pearson Education, Inc., publishing as Pearson Prentice Hall. All rights reserved.

Concept Connector Study Guide
GEOGRAPHY'S IMPACT (continued)

C. Sample Topics for Thematic Essays

Below are examples of thematic essay topics that might appear on a test. Prepare for the test by outlining an essay for each topic on a separate sheet of paper. Use the Concept Connector Handbooks at the end of your textbook, as well as chapter information, to outline your essays.

1. Select two cities or countries whose locations have helped in their military defense. Discuss each location and describe how geography made foreign invasions more difficult. You may consider Paris, England, Japan, or other locations.

2. How did Britain's location and climate help it rise to global prominence from 1700 to 1800?

3. Explain how the availability of natural resources helped Great Britain and the United States become leaders in the Industrial Revolution.

4. How has geography posed a challenge to unity in Indonesia?

5. Describe how the location of the United States and Latin America led to the development of the Monroe Doctrine and the Roosevelt Corollary and how these policies shaped the relationship between the United States and Latin America.

6. Explain why the location of the Ottoman empire made it a desirable ally during World War I. How did its decision to join the Central Powers affect the war?

7. Why does the location of the Middle East make it the focus of many conflicts in the modern world?

8. Describe how desertification affected early migrations in Africa and how it may affect Africa's future.

© Pearson Education, Inc., publishing as Pearson Prentice Hall. All rights reserved.

Concept Connector Study Guide

Migration

Essential Question: What factors cause large groups of people to move from one place to another?

A. Define *migration*. _____

_____

_____

B. *Record information about the topics listed in the Cumulative Review or your answers to the questions in the Cumulative Review below. Use the Concept Connector Handbooks at the end of your textbook, as well as chapter information, to complete this worksheet.*

1. **Migrations of Early People**

   Hominids, a group that includes humans and their closest relatives, all walk upright on two feet. Humans are the only hominids that live today. Two hominid groups, *Homo erectus* and *Homo sapiens*, migrated from Africa to Europe and Asia. Early humans were nomads, or people who move from place to place to find food. It is likely that during the periods of prehistory and very early history, the same factors influenced migration. For example, people migrated in search of plants and animals for food. Climate change and other environmental events, such as droughts, landslides, earthquakes, or volcanic eruptions, might also have caused people to migrate. Changes in population or competition for resources among groups of people are often factors in migration, too.

2. **Indo-European Migrations**

   The Aryans were one of many groups of speakers of Indo-European languages who migrated across Europe and Asia. The migration of the Aryans into India affected the culture of India in many ways. For example, the beliefs of the Aryans influenced the development of Hinduism and the caste system in India. The language of the Aryans developed into Sanskrit, the Indian language used for sacred writings. Other Indo-Europeans groups include the Celts, Germans, and Italics. You can see by the names of these other Indo-European groups that they influenced the development of culture in Europe.

3. **Migration and Language**

   Scholars are able to trace migrations by studying language patterns. Many people of European descent speak one of the varieties of languages that can be traced to a common Indo-European language. Scholars have learned that West African farmers and herders migrated to the south and east between 1000 B.C. and A.D. 1000. They spoke a variety of languages derived from a single common language. The root language is Bantu, which gives this movement its name, the Bantu migrations. As they migrated in southern Africa, the Bantu-speakers spread their skills in farming, ironworking, and domesticating animals. The influence of the Bantu-speakers is still found in the languages of the region today.

© Pearson Education, Inc., publishing as Pearson Prentice Hall. All rights reserved.

Concept Connector Study Guide
MIGRATION *(continued)*

4. Westward Movement in the United States (Chapter 8, page 281)

_____

_____

_____

_____

_____

_____

_____

_____

_____

5. Factors in European Migration to the Americas (Chapter 8, page 281)

_____

_____

_____

_____

_____

_____

_____

_____

_____

© Pearson Education, Inc., publishing as Pearson Prentice Hall. All rights reserved.

Concept Connector Study Guide
MIGRATION *(continued)*

C. Sample Topics for Thematic Essays

Below are examples of thematic essay topics that might appear on a test. Prepare for the test by outlining an essay for each topic on a separate sheet of paper. Use the Concept Connector Handbooks at the end of your textbook, as well as chapter information, to outline your essays.

1. Select at least two instances between 1700 and 1950 where groups were "pushed" to migrate from one area to another. Describe the reasons why they migrated, and discuss how the groups adapted to the migration and how their move affected the area to which they moved.

2. Compare and contrast the "pull" factors that brought Europeans to the Americas between 1600 and 1800 with the "pull" factors that encouraged movement to the western United States between 1800 and 1900.

3. Identify and discuss at least three factors that "pushed" or "pulled" people into growing cities in Europe and the Americas between 1800 and 1900.

4. Identify and discuss at least three factors that cause people to migrate today. Give an example of each and describe the conditions that have encouraged migration.

5. Explain the role of religion in the partition of India in 1948 and in the migration of people that resulted.

6. Identify the "push" factor that brought the first large group of Europeans to Australia and the "pull" factors that drew others there during the late 1800s.

7. Evaluate how the potato famine in Ireland (which began in 1845) and the resulting migration of a million Irish people affected Ireland's relationships with the United States and Great Britain.

8. Compare and contrast the forced migration in southern Sudan and the forced migration in Sudan's Darfur region.

© Pearson Education, Inc., publishing as Pearson Prentice Hall. All rights reserved.

Name_____ Class_____ Date_____

Concept Connector Study Guide

Nationalism

Essential Question: How have people used nationalism as a basis for their actions?

A. Define *nationalism*. _____

_____

_____

B. *Record information about the topics listed in the Cumulative Review or your answers to the questions in the Cumulative Review below. Use the Concept Connector Handbooks at the end of your textbook, as well as chapter information, to complete this worksheet.*

1. Nationalism in the American Revolution (Chapter 3, page 139)

_____

_____

_____

_____

2. Latin American Nationalism and French Nationalism (Chapter 4, page 163)

_____

_____

_____

_____

3. Unification and Nationalism in Greece and Italy (Chapter 7, page 253)

_____

_____

_____

_____

4. Revolts in the Balkans (Chapter 7, page 253)

_____

_____

_____

_____

© Pearson Education, Inc., publishing as Pearson Prentice Hall. All rights reserved.

Concept Connector Study Guide
NATIONALISM (continued)

5. English Nationalism (Chapter 9, page 315)

_____

_____

_____

_____

_____

6. Nationalism in the United States (Chapter 9, page 315)

_____

_____

_____

_____

_____

7. Pan-Arab and Pan-Slav Nationalism (Chapter 12, page 415)

_____

_____

_____

_____

_____

8. Expansion in Japan, the United States, and Britain (Chapter 12, page 415)

_____

_____

_____

_____

_____

9. Hindu Nationalism of the BJP in India (Chapter 16, page 575)

_____

_____

_____

_____

_____

© Pearson Education, Inc., publishing as Pearson Prentice Hall. All rights reserved.

Concept Connector Study Guide

NATIONALISM *(continued)*

C. Sample Topics for Thematic Essays

Below are examples of thematic essay topics that might appear on a test. Prepare for the test by outlining an essay for each topic on a separate sheet of paper. Use the Concept Connector Handbooks at the end of your textbook, as well as chapter information, to outline your essays.

1. Compare and contrast the ways in which nationalism helped Napoleon create an empire and how it also encouraged resistance against that empire.

2. Discuss the role of nationalism in the revolts by slaves, creoles, and others in South and Central America in the late 1700s and early 1800s.

3. Describe how Bismarck used nationalism to attack both the Catholic Church and socialists in the late 1800s and the results of those attacks.

4. Explain the effects of nationalist movements on the Hapsburg empire before and after 1848 and how the success of the Hungarians after 1866 continued to weaken the empire.

5. Describe the British response to nationalists in India before and after World War I and how Mohandas Gandhi helped inspire Indians to work for an independent nation.

6. Discuss how Mussolini used nationalism to gain and keep power in Italy.

7. Describe how Adolf Hitler used nationalism to help him gain control of the country and establish the Third Reich.

8. Describe the role of nationalism in the conflict that broke out in the former Yugoslavia in the 1990s.

© Pearson Education, Inc., publishing as Pearson Prentice Hall. All rights reserved.

Concept Connector Study Guide

People and the Environment

Essential Question: What impact have people had on the environment?

A. Define *environment.* _____

_____

_____

B. *Record information about the topics listed in the Cumulative Review or your answers to the questions in the Cumulative Review below. Use the Concept Connector Handbooks at the end of your textbook, as well as chapter information, to complete this worksheet.*

1. Stone Age Hominids and Neolithic Farmers

Stone Age people were nomads who moved from place to place to find food. In general, men hunted or fished while the women and children gathered berries, fruits, nuts, grains, and roots. Although Stone Age people depended on their environment for survival, they also adapted their surroundings to their needs. They made tools from stone, bone, or wood—materials they found at hand. They made clothing from the skins of animals. They may have used boats or canoes to travel across water. Neolithic farmers adapted the environment to a greater extent than did earlier Stone Age peoples. They settled in one place, selecting particular plants to cultivate for food. They used animals such as oxen or water buffaloes to plow the fields. They used clay to create pottery and wove cloth from animal hair or plant fibers.

2. The Building of Tenochtitlán

The capital city of the Aztec, Tenochtitlán, was built on an island in a lake. The Aztec built temples, palaces, zoos, and floating gardens, turning the island into a magnificent city. As they filled the lake with floating gardens called chinampas, they created canals for transportation. To connect the city with the mainland, they built wide stone causeways. From this city, the Aztec governed a complex, well-ordered empire.

© Pearson Education, Inc., publishing as Pearson Prentice Hall. All rights reserved.

Concept Connector Study Guide

PEOPLE AND THE ENVIRONMENT (continued)

3. Farming Methods

Civilizations in the Americas developed different farming techniques based on their environment. The Maya of Mesoamerica developed two farming methods that helped them grow crops in their tropical environment. In the first method, farmers burned down forests, then cleared the land to plant it. In the second method, farmers built raised fields along the banks of rivers. This lifted the crops above the annual floods. The Aztec settled on an island in a lake. They developed a farming method that allowed them to grow crops on human-made islands. On these artificial islands, the Aztec grew maize, squash, and beans. The Inca lived in the mountains of South America. To farm, they carved terraces, or flat strips of land, on steep hillsides. Stone walls held the terraces in place. The terraces provided flat land for crops and kept rains from washing the soil away. The Hohokam lived in the desert southwest of North America. To grow crops they created a complex irrigation system. Canals carried river water to fields over as much as ten miles.

4. Geoglyphs

The way that people affect the environment does not always appear to have a practical application. For example, between 500 B.C. and A.D. 500, the Nazca people lived along the southern coast of Peru. They etched geoglyphs in the desert. A geoglyph is a figure or line made on Earth's surface by clearing away rocks and soil. Some Nazca geoglyphs extend for miles. The designs include giant birds, whales, and spiders. Most researchers think the geoglyphs had spiritual significance.

5. Cliff Dwellings and Earthworks

In North America between A.D. 1150 and A.D. 1300, the Anasazi constructed huge housing complexes on cliffs along the sides of sheer canyon walls. These cliff dwellings offered protection from enemies. The Anasazi cut blocks from stone to build the dwellings. They used ladders to reach their fields on the flatlands above or the canyon floor below. One of the largest dwellings had more than 200 rooms. Other Native American groups, the Adena and the Hopewell, affected the environment in a different way. They built giant earthworks by heaping earth in piles and shaping them. Some of the earthworks were burial mounds, others were used as the platforms for temples, or formed defensive walls. Some were in the shape of an animal. The Adena's Great Serpent Mound twists in the shape of a snake for almost a quarter of a mile.

© Pearson Education, Inc., publishing as Pearson Prentice Hall. All rights reserved.

Concept Connector Study Guide
PEOPLE AND THE ENVIRONMENT *(continued)*

C. Sample Topics for Thematic Essays

Below are examples of thematic essay topics that might appear on a test. Prepare for the test by outlining an essay for each topic on a separate sheet of paper. Use the Concept Connector Handbooks at the end of your textbook, as well as chapter information, to outline your essays.

1. Discuss the relationship between the natural environment and industrialization in the period between 1750 and 1914.

2. Explain how British rule in India affected the natural environment.

3. Evaluate the positive and negative effects of automobiles on people's lives and on the environment.

4. Compare and contrast the conditions in North American and European cities during the Industrial Revolution with those in South American and Asian cities today.

5. Discuss how increased industrialization has threatened air and water quality and how governments have responded.

6. Describe some of the environmental threats facing Africa, and discuss the causes of these threats. What are some possible solutions to these environmental problems?

7. Discuss how nuclear power could help the environment as well as ways it could harm it.

8. Describe how global warming might harm the environment as well as how limiting emissions of greenhouse gases could hamper economic growth.

© Pearson Education, Inc., publishing as Pearson Prentice Hall. All rights reserved.

Concept Connector Study Guide

Political Systems

Essential Question: How have societies chosen to govern themselves?

A. Define *political system.* _____

_____

_____

B. *Record information about the topics listed in the Cumulative Review or your answers to the questions in the Cumulative Review below. Use the Concept Connector Handbooks at the end of your textbook, as well as chapter information, to complete this worksheet.*

1. Oligarchy

In ancient Greece, between 750 B.C. and 500 B.C., different forms of government evolved. The first cities were ruled by kings. A government in which a hereditary ruler has central power is called a monarchy. Wealthy landowners could afford bronze weapons and chariots. They were the military defenders of the city. Gradually they won power for themselves; this resulted in an aristocracy, or government by a hereditary landholding elite. As trade grew, a new middle class of wealthy merchants, farmers, and artisans developed in some cities. They challenged the aristocracy for power. The result in some city-states was a form of government called an oligarchy. In an oligarchy, power is in the hands of a small, wealthy elite.

2. The Roman Republic and the Oligarchies of Ancient Greece

In the oligarchies of ancient Greece, power was in the hands of a small, wealthy elite. Ancient Romans set up a different form of government. In 509 B.C., wealthy Roman landowners overthrew the king. In place of a monarchy, the Romans established a republic. Men who were citizens could elect their officials. Three groups of citizens helped govern the republic—the senate, the magistrates, and several assemblies. Early Rome was made up of two social orders: the wealthy landowning patricians and the plebeians. Although both plebeians and patricians voted, only patricians could be elected to office. Even in the republic, power generally remained in the hands of the wealthy ruling class.

© Pearson Education, Inc., publishing as Pearson Prentice Hall. All rights reserved.

Concept Connector Study Guide
POLITICAL SYSTEMS *(continued)*

3. Religion and Rulers in Egypt, China, and the Inca Empire

In early civilizations, religious beliefs and political systems were often linked. In ancient Egypt, the chief god was the sun god, Amon-Re. The pharaohs, whom Egyptians viewed as gods as well as kings, were believed to receive their right to rule from Amon-Re. In China, rulers were not considered gods. Instead, the Chinese developed the idea of the Mandate of Heaven. This was the divine right to rule. As long as a dynasty provided good government, it was believed the gods wanted that dynasty to continue. If rulers became corrupt or weak, the Chinese believed that heaven would withdraw its support. In the chaos that followed, a new leader would seize power. If the new leader was successful, it showed the people that the new dynasty had won the Mandate of Heaven. In the Andes of South America, the Incan civilization grew into an empire in the 1400s. The Inca believed their emperor was divine, descended from the sun itself. Incan emperors had absolute power and also served as the religious leaders of the empire.

4. Feudalism and Building a Strong Empire

Feudalism was a political system in which powerful lords divided their landhold-ings among lesser lords in exchange for loyalty and service. Around 220 B.C., the emperor Shi Huangdi abolished feudalism in China in order to create a strong central government. He felt that allegiances to local lords weakened the central government. Feudalism was the political system of medieval Europe for hundreds of years. Knights owed military service to their feudal lords. Warfare was constant because rival lords battled for power. Gradually feudalism declined. Monarchs became more powerful. Knights were replaced by professional armies. Towns and cities provided revenue for kings. Kings gained the right to tax their subjects, and strong centralized governments began to form. In both China and Europe, monarchies replaced the political system of feudalism.

5. Absolute Monarchy Under Louis XIV and Imperial Rule in Ancient Rome

Absolute monarchy in France under Louis XIV and imperial rule in ancient Rome were similar in some respects. In both systems, political power was in the hands of a central figure. Louis XIV claimed divine right to rule. Some Roman emperors were worshiped as gods after death if they ruled well. Louis XIV did not once call a meeting of the Estates General, which was a council made up of representatives of all French social classes. In imperial Rome, the senate, an elected body, contin-ued to meet, but in reality it had little power. As a symbol of his power, Louis XIV called himself the Sun King and turned the palace of Versailles into the most mag-nificent building in Europe. Roman symbols of power included beautiful monu-ments, temples, and public buildings throughout the capital city.

© Pearson Education, Inc., publishing as Pearson Prentice Hall. All rights reserved.

Concept Connector Study Guide

POLITICAL SYSTEMS *(continued)*

6. Government Under an Absolute Monarch (Chapter 1, page 49)

_____

_____

_____

_____

_____

_____

_____

7. The Federal Government (Chapter 2, page 77)

_____

_____

_____

_____

_____

_____

_____

8. Enlightenment Ideas About Democracy and Totalitarianism
(Chapter 13, page 455)

_____

_____

_____

_____

_____

_____

_____

© Pearson Education, Inc., publishing as Pearson Prentice Hall. All rights reserved.

Concept Connector Study Guide

POLITICAL SYSTEMS *(continued)*

C. Sample Topics for Thematic Essays

Below are examples of thematic essay topics that might appear on a test. Prepare for the test by outlining an essay for each topic on a separate sheet of paper. Use the Concept Connector Handbooks at the end of your textbook, as well as chapter information, to outline your essays.

1. Compare and contrast democracy in ancient Athens with the American political system today, including the responsibilities of citizens.

2. Describe the political system in England after the Magna Carta and the establishment of Parliament in the 1300s.

3. Compare monarchy to aristocracy. How are these two political systems similar? How are they different? Include an example of each from history in your essay.

4. Describe the relationship between the Industrial Revolution and the ideas of Karl Marx, and discuss the reasons why communism appealed to many workers of this time.

5. Describe the changes to Argentina's political system that occurred between the early 1900s and the late 1900s.

6. Analyze the conditions in Eastern Europe and the Soviet Union late in the Cold War that led to the collapse of communism and the breakup of the Soviet Union.

7. Describe the changes in the political system in South Africa after the end of apartheid.

8. Describe the changes that occurred to the Iraqi political system after the defeat of Saddam Hussein in 2003. What challenges does the new political system face?

© Pearson Education, Inc., publishing as Pearson Prentice Hall. All rights reserved.

Concept Connector Study Guide

Revolution

Essential Question: Why have political revolutions occurred?

A. Define *revolution.* _____

_____

_____

B. *Record information about the topics listed in the Cumulative Review or your answers to the questions in the Cumulative Review below. Use the Concept Connector Handbooks at the end of your textbook, as well as chapter information, to complete this worksheet.*

1. The Transfer of Power in England, 1377–1688
By the 1660s, England had recently experienced a civil war and the execution of a monarch. When the current king, James II, suspended laws and appointed Catholics to high offices, Protestant leaders in England invited James' Protestant daughter, Mary, and her husband, William, to rule. James II fled the country. This bloodless overthrow of the monarch became known as the Glorious Revolution. This was a radical event for its time because the transfer of power had never been accomplished by Parliament in this way before, nor with so little violence. The Glorious Revolution created a type of government known as a limited monarchy, in which a constitution or legislative body limits the monarch's powers. Additionally, before they could rule, William and Mary had to accept several acts by Parliament known as the English Bill of Rights.

2. The German Peasants' Revolt of 1524 and the French Revolution
(Chapter 3, page 139)

_____

_____

_____

_____

_____

3. Latin American Revolutions (Chapter 4, page 163)

_____

_____

_____

_____

_____

© Pearson Education, Inc., publishing as Pearson Prentice Hall. All rights reserved.

Concept Connector Study Guide
REVOLUTION *(continued)*

4. **The Russian Revolution and the French Revolution** (Chapter 11, page 383)

_____

_____

_____

_____

_____

_____

_____

5. **European Colonial Independence Between 1946 and 1970 and the American Revolution** (Chapter 16, page 575)

_____

_____

_____

_____

_____

_____

_____

6. **Recent Rebellions in Latin America and Earlier Revolutions** (Chapter 18, page 627)

_____

_____

_____

_____

_____

_____

_____

© Pearson Education, Inc., publishing as Pearson Prentice Hall. All rights reserved.

Concept Connector Study Guide
REVOLUTION *(continued)*

C. Sample Topics for Thematic Essays

Below are examples of thematic essay topics that might appear on a test. Prepare for the test by outlining an essay for each topic on a separate sheet of paper. Use the Concept Connector Handbooks at the end of your textbook, as well as chapter information, to outline your essays.

1. Describe how plebeians helped change the Roman republic and how their opposition to rulers helped create the Roman empire.

2. Describe the system of government in England during the early 1200s, when rebellious barons forced King John to sign the Magna Carta, and the effect on government in the following years.

3. Describe the causes of the Meiji Restoration, which swept the shogun from power in 1868 in Japan.

4. Discuss the basic dispute between monarchs and Parliament in England in the 1600s and how it resulted in the English Civil War and the Glorious Revolution.

5. Discuss the economic problems of the Third Estate before the French Revolution and how these problems inspired people to revolt.

6. Discuss the causes and effects of the revolution and the civil war that put Vladimir Lenin in power in Russia by 1921.

7. Contrast the tactics used by Mohandas Gandhi during the struggle for independence in India with tactics used by other revolutionary leaders before the start of World War II.

8. Describe the social and economic conditions in South Africa during most of the twentieth century and how other countries around the world helped bring about change there.

© Pearson Education, Inc., publishing as Pearson Prentice Hall. All rights reserved.

Concept Connector Study Guide

Science

Essential Question: How has science changed people's lives throughout history?

A. Define *science.* _____

_____

_____

B. *Record information about the topics listed in the Cumulative Review or your answers to the questions in the Cumulative Review below. Use the Concept Connector Handbooks at the end of your textbook, as well as chapter information, to complete this worksheet.*

1. Advances in Mathematics

Advances in mathematics and science developed by early civilizations benefit us today. The Greeks contributed geometry, astronomical observations, and practical inventions based on physics. Indian civilizations contributed the system of writing numbers, including zero, that we use today. In China during the Han dynasty, scientists wrote texts on chemistry, zoology, botany, and other subjects. The Chinese also pioneered advanced methods of shipbuilding and invented the rudder to steer. Other practical inventions from China include fishing reels, suspension bridges, and a method for making paper. Why were such advances possible in these ancient societies? They all had stable governments, periods of peace and prosperity, and opportunities for education.

2. Incan Surgery

Civilizations of the Americas made many important advances. The Inca, for example, practiced medical procedures that are similar to those currently used in modern medicine. Surgical techniques practiced by the Inca included surgery on the human skull. They cleaned the area to be operated on and gave the patient a drug to make him or her unconscious. These procedures are similar to the modern use of antiseptics and anesthesia.

3. The Ideas of Copernicus and Newton

In 1543, Polish scholar Nicolaus Copernicus proposed his heliocentric, or sun-centered, model of the universe. His theory was rejected, in part, because it questioned the system of knowledge that rested on the work of classical thinkers such as Ptolemy. About 100 years later, Isaac Newton developed theories about gravity and the workings of the universe. Newton's ideas were not rejected. What had changed? In the years between Copernicus and Newton, a new approach to science had emerged. It was called the scientific method, and it was based on observation and experimentation. It was actually a revolution in thought. Scientists still depend on this step-by-step process of discovery.

© Pearson Education, Inc., publishing as Pearson Prentice Hall. All rights reserved.

Concept Connector Study Guide

SCIENCE *(continued)*

4. The Scientific Revolution and the Scientific Ideas of the Late 1800s
(Chapter 6, page 223)

_____

_____

_____

_____

_____

_____

_____

_____

5. Newton's Theories and Einstein's Theories (Chapter 13, page 455)

_____

_____

_____

_____

_____

_____

_____

_____

6. Louis Pasteur's Medical Advances and Those of World War II
(Chapter 14, page 495)

_____

_____

_____

_____

_____

_____

_____

_____

© Pearson Education, Inc., publishing as Pearson Prentice Hall. All rights reserved.

Concept Connector Study Guide
SCIENCE (continued)

C. Sample Topics for Thematic Essays

Below are examples of thematic essay topics that might appear on a test. Prepare for the test by outlining an essay for each topic on a separate sheet of paper. Use the Concept Connector Handbooks at the end of your textbook, as well as chapter information, to outline your essays.

1. Explain the role the Scientific Revolution played in the development of the Enlightenment.

2. Describe how "germ theory" helped improve health in the 1800s, and discuss how new medical and health practices contributed to the growth in population.

3. Discuss the scientific knowledge that changed medical care in hospitals during the 1800s and how it improved health care, especially for poor people.

4. Describe the scientific discoveries made during the 1900s by Marie Curie, Albert Einstein, and Enrico Fermi. What were the effects of these discoveries?

5. What did the work of genetic researchers in the 1950s reveal about DNA? What were the implications of these discoveries?

6. Explain how science has been used to explore and make use of space.

7. Discuss the effect of computers on society and modern life and the reasons why this period is sometimes called "The Information Age."

8. Describe some benefits of biotechnology and genetic engineering, as well as some issues that create debate about these topics.

© Pearson Education, Inc., publishing as Pearson Prentice Hall. All rights reserved.

Concept Connector Study Guide

Technology

Essential Question: How has technology changed the way people live and work?

A. Define *technology*. _____
_____
_____

B. *Record information about the topics listed in the Cumulative Review or your answers to the questions in the Cumulative Review below. Use the Concept Connector Handbooks at the end of your textbook, as well as chapter information, to complete this worksheet.*

1. **Paleolithic Stone Tools**
   People of the Old Stone Age, or Paleolithic Period, made tools out of materials at hand, such as stone, wood, or bone. Tools were often made from flint because the stone is relatively easy to shape by chipping flakes from it. Once chipped, these stones have sharp edges. Creating a tool required patience, skill, strength, and a number of other tools. The toolmaker would use a hard stone to strike flakes off another stone, and then use other tools, such as a small chisel, to refine the tool's shape. Even stone tools from locations far apart were made with similar techniques. The use of tools indicates people were developing complex technologies to survive, and probably used spoken language to communicate techniques.

2. **Advances During Prehistory and Technological Advances in Egypt and Mesopotamia**
   During prehistory, technological advances such as the development of stone tools, domestication of animals, and farming allowed early humans to radically expand the possibilities for their lives. The peoples of ancient Mesopotamia and Egypt also made important advances. In Mesopotamia, people turned iron into powerful weapons and developed a writing system called cuneiform. Egyptians made a type of paper from plants and developed a cursive writing system. Medications made from plants helped to heal and ease symptoms. Did the advances of prehistory or the advances of Mesopotamia and Egypt have a greater impact? You could make the argument that all later advances are just improvements or refinements of technologies developed during prehistory.

3. **Military Technology and the Ottoman and Safavid Empires**
   The Ottoman and Safavid empires benefited from advances in military technology. The Ottoman fleet helped to conquer Constantinople. Both empires used cannons to blast defensive walls, while muskets increased the effectiveness of their foot soldiers. The new military technology helped the Ottomans expand in the lands surrounding the Mediterranean, while the Safavids built a strong empire in Persia. As a result, the period from about 1450 to 1650 is sometimes called "the age of gunpowder empires."

© Pearson Education, Inc., publishing as Pearson Prentice Hall. All rights reserved.

Concept Connector Study Guide

TECHNOLOGY *(continued)*

4. The Printing Press

The invention of the printing press in Europe changed the course of history. Because of this technology, books became cheaper and more readily available. Literacy increased. As presses were established in Europe, printed books exposed literate Europeans to new concepts and encouraged the exchange of ideas. Many of the first printing technologies, however, were not developed in Europe, but in China. For example, in the 700s the Chinese developed block printing. In block printing, a full page of characters was carved onto a wooden block. Later, in the 1040s, they invented movable type. With movable type, precut characters were combined to form a page.

5. Gunpowder

Gunpowder was developed by the Chinese about 850. The earliest form of gunpowder was made from a mixture of saltpeter, sulfur, and charcoal, all found in abundance in China. The gunpowder was first used in fireworks. Later, gunpowder was used in cannons. The use of cannons during the Hundred Years' War in Europe helped to end feudal society. Castles could not stand up to the more destructive firepower. Monarchs needed large armies, not feudal vassals, to fight their wars.

6. The Compass

In the 1400s, European knowledge of the world, and how to navigate it, greatly expanded. Navigators began to use existing instruments like the compass in new ways. The compass became a customary navigational tool in the 1400s. The magnetic compass uses an iron needle, which is magnetized by a lodestone, to align with Earth's north and south poles. Navigators used the compass to find their bearings and chart courses.

7. The Printing Press and the Steam Engine (Chapter 5, page 191)

_____

_____

_____

_____

_____

8. The Agricultural Revolution and the Industrial Revolution (Chapter 6, page 223)

_____

_____

_____

_____

_____

© Pearson Education, Inc., publishing as Pearson Prentice Hall. All rights reserved.

Concept Connector Study Guide

TECHNOLOGY *(continued)*

9. First and Second Phases of the Industrial Revolution (Chapter 6, page 223)

_____
_____
_____
_____
_____
_____

10. Nuclear Power (Chapter 14, page 495)

_____
_____
_____
_____
_____
_____

11. Coal Mines, Factories, and Railroads in Europe and North America in the 1800s and Hydroelectric Power in Africa Today (Chapter 18, page 627)

_____
_____
_____
_____
_____
_____

12. The Telephone and Computer Technology (Chapter 19, page 663)

_____
_____
_____
_____
_____
_____

© Pearson Education, Inc., publishing as Pearson Prentice Hall. All rights reserved.

Concept Connector Study Guide

TECHNOLOGY *(continued)*

C. Sample Topics for Thematic Essays

Below are examples of thematic essay topics that might appear on a test. Prepare for the test by outlining an essay for each topic on a separate sheet of paper. Use the Concept Connector Handbooks at the end of your textbook, as well as chapter information, to outline your essays.

1. Describe new sources of energy and new materials and how they helped businesses change the way work was done in the 1700s.

2. Describe the "putting-out system" used to produce textiles in Britain in the 1600s and how it was changed by new technology in the 1700s.

3. Discuss how the use of steam power changed land and sea transportation during the 1800s and how it expanded business opportunities and personal travel.

4. Compare the benefits of industrialization with the problems it created.

5. How did Henry Ford revolutionize the automobile industry? How did the rise of the automobile change industrialized societies?

6. Discuss the reasons why the United States used the atomic bomb in World War II and how its development by the Soviet Union within a few years affected world politics.

7. Discuss how improvements in transportation technology have contributed to the success of Japan and "the Asian tigers" since the end of World War II.

8. Describe the role of artificial satellites in the modern world, and discuss at least two ways they affect everyday life.

© Pearson Education, Inc., publishing as Pearson Prentice Hall. All rights reserved.

Concept Connector Study Guide

Trade

Essential Question: What have been the major trade networks in world history?

A. Define *trade.* _____

_____

_____

B. *Record information about the topics listed in the Cumulative Review or your answers to the questions in the Cumulative Review below. Use the Concept Connector Handbooks at the end of your textbook, as well as chapter information, to complete this worksheet.*

1. **Phoenician Sea Traders**
   While powerful rulers controlled large empires in the ancient Middle East, the smaller state of Phoenicia made its own contribution to civilization. The Phoenicians gained fame as both sailors and traders. They produced glass from coastal sand, and a luxurious dye called "Tyrian purple" from a tiny sea snail. The Phoenicians traded all around the Mediterranean Sea, and as far as Britain. To promote trade, they established colonies in North Africa, Sicily, and Spain. The Phoenicians spread Middle Eastern civilization all around the Mediterranean. One of their most significant cultural contributions is the Phoenician alphabet. It is the basis of the alphabet we use today.

2. **Phoenician Trade Network and the Silk Road**
   The Phoenicians were Middle Eastern sea traders who sailed around the Mediterranean and a far as Spain. The Silk Road was a land-based network of trade routes that connected China to the Mediterranean. Both trade routes connected multiple cultures. The Phoenician trade network depended on Phoenician ships, traders, and the trade posts and colonies they set up. The Silk Road, on the other hand, was not controlled by any one group. In addition, trade goods on the Silk Road exchanged hands often because they passed from trader to trader on the extensive route. Small, expensive, luxury items were traded, including silk and spices from the east, and Roman glass from the west. They took up less space, were easier to carry, and had high value.

3. **Trade in Ancient Greece and Phoenicia**
   The culture and economy of ancient Greece was greatly influenced by trade. With hundreds of bays offering safe harbor for ships, and thousands of miles of coastline, it was only natural that Greeks became expert sailors. Greek ships carried cargoes of olive oil, wine, and marble throughout the eastern Mediterranean. They returned not only with grains and metals but also with ideas, which they adapted to their own needs. By focusing on the eastern Mediterranean, Greek sailors never traveled as far as the Phoenicians. Phoenicians, who made their home on the eastern shore of the Mediterranean, sailed across the length of the Mediterranean into the Atlantic Ocean to reach the west coast of North Africa and as far north as Britain.

© Pearson Education, Inc., publishing as Pearson Prentice Hall. All rights reserved.

Concept Connector Study Guide
TRADE (continued)

4. Traders and Merchants in Feudalism and the Manorial System

Medieval Europe was dominated by feudalism and the manorial system. Feudalism was a political system; the manor, or lord's estate, was an economic system. Both systems were based on mutual obligations. The manor was intended to be self-sufficient, producing everything needed by the lord's family and the peasants and serfs who lived there. How did trade develop during this period? Around the 1100s, people began to travel more; crusaders brought luxury goods back to Europe. Nobles wanted goods that could not be produced on manors, and peasants needed iron for farm tools. Traders formed merchant companies that traveled together and set up trade fairs near major crossroads. Slowly, small trade settlements in Europe developed into towns and cities. Meanwhile, Europe's population was growing. Manors became overcrowded. Lords often allowed peasants to buy their freedom and move to towns.

5. Trade in the Byzantine Empire, Russia, and Phoenicia

Trade was at the heart of the prosperity and power of Constantinople and the Byzantine empire. In Russia, trade contributed to the rise of Kiev and Moscow. Earlier, trade had been just as important to the ancient Phoenicians. Location helped each of these cities or regions develop trade. Phoenicia was located on the eastern coast of the Mediterranean. In addition, Phoenicia had a resource that people wanted, a valuable purple dye. The Byzantine empire had a strategic location between Europe and Asia, in an area linking the Mediterranean and Black seas. From this location, the empire commanded key trade routes. Merchants bought and sold wheat from Egypt, silks from China, spices from Southeast Asia, and furs from Vikings in Scandinavia. Rivers connected Vikings with Kiev and Russia. Russia's network of rivers connected it to the advanced Byzantine world Eventually Russia adopted many aspects of Byzantine culture.

6. Coastal Peoples and Trade

Naturally, many coastal peoples became skilled sailors and developed major trading cultures. Greek, Viking, and East African traders all sailed great distances using their nautical skills, and exchanged goods and ideas with new cultures. The Mediterranean and the Aegean seas were central to the development of Greece, and the seas provided a vital link to the world outside. The Greeks traded primarily in the eastern Mediterranean. Farmland was limited in Greece. When the population grew, the Greeks set up colonies throughout the Mediterranean, including in Spain and Egypt. These colonies expanded trade opportunities for the Greeks. The Vikings of Scandinavia were warriors, skilled shipbuilders, and sailors. They constructed shallow-draft ships that could sail up European rivers, which allowed them to attack far inland. Eventually, Viking groups settled outside of Scandinavia and influenced the development of cultures in Russia and Normandy, among other places. East African trading cities flourished in the 600s. From ancient times, Phoenician, Greek, Roman, and Indian traders traded in the region. Later, African rulers allowed Arab and Persian merchants to set up communities. East African trading cities benefited from the monsoon winds that carried ships between Africa and India. Goods from the interior of Africa, Persia, Arabia, India, China, and Southwest Asia flowed on and off the shores of East Africa.

© Pearson Education, Inc., publishing as Pearson Prentice Hall. All rights reserved.

Concept Connector Study Guide
TRADE *(continued)*

7. Chinese Trade in Southern China and Up Coast

During his reign, the famous Han emperor Wudi (141 B.C–87 B.C) opened up a vast trade network, later called the Silk Road, that linked China to the west. Under both the Tang and Song dynasties, foreign trade flourished, with Chinese merchants carrying goods to Southeast Asia in exchange for spices, rare woods, and a faster-growing type of rice. Between 1405 and 1433, a Chinese admiral named Zheng He commanded a series of sea expeditions to promote trade. He sailed to the Red Sea and the Persian Gulf and visited ports in East Africa. As a result of trade, Chinese merchants settled permanently in Southeast Asia and India, bringing their culture with them.

8. The Dutch Trading Empire

In the early 1600s, the Dutch set up what became a powerful trading empire in Southeast Asia. It was actually a trading company known as the Dutch East India Company. Unlike the companies of other European companies, the Dutch East India Company had full sovereign powers. Because it had the power to build armies, wage war, negotiate peace treaties, and govern overseas territory, it came to dominate the region. In 1641, the Dutch captured Malacca from the Portuguese and opened trade with China. Soon they were able to enforce a monopoly in the Spice Islands. The Dutch maintained an empire in Indonesia until the 1900s.

9. Indian Trade in Southeast Asia

The Mughal dynasty ruled in India from 1526 to 1857. Mughal India was the center of a valuable spice trade. It was also the world leader in textile manufacturing, exporting large quantities of silk and cotton cloth. The Mughal empire was large and powerful. When Europeans approached Mughal emperors about trading rights, the Mughals saw no threat in granting them. The Portuguese, Dutch, English, and French were allowed to build forts and warehouses in Indian coastal towns. As the empire weakened, however, the Europeans fought for greater control. By the late 1700s, the British East India Company used its great wealth to dominate most of India.

10. European Approaches to Trade in the 1500s and 1600s

In the 1500s and 1600s, European countries took various approaches to trade. The Portuguese did not set up colonies. Instead, they set up coastal trading posts with just enough men and firepower to defend them. They also attacked existing trading centers to add to their vast trading empire. As Portuguese power declined, the British, French, and Dutch established permanent footholds. In general, these nations established closer ties with local rulers, sometimes negotiating trade treaties. However, European trading companies were willing to use force and did. They also attempted to convert Asians and Africans to Christianity, sometimes destroying local sacred sites.

© Pearson Education, Inc., publishing as Pearson Prentice Hall. All rights reserved.

Concept Connector Study Guide
TRADE *(continued)*

11. Earlier Slave Trades and the Atlantic Slave Trade
The slave trade reached its height after the age of exploration, when Europe's overseas colonies required huge numbers of laborers to grow cash crops. However, the slave trade had existed long before this time. For example, slavery existed in ancient Egypt, Greece, and Rome, as well as in the Muslim world. In these cultures, slaves were often conquered peoples. Sometimes, to pay debts, an individual might sell himself as a slave. The ancient Egyptians may have used slaves to build the great pyramids. As Rome expanded, it strained its workforce. As a result, Rome was heavily dependent on slaves. In the Muslim world, slaves were generally well treated. The founder of Islam, Muhammad, urged his followers to be kind to their slaves. The Atlantic slave trade however, was on a much larger scale and, in many ways, the most cruel. Unlike most other types of slavery, it was racially based, and entailed the forced migration of about 13 million people from Africa.

12. Trade Within the Roman Empire (Chapter 1, page 49)

_____

_____

_____

_____

_____

13. Railroad Travel and Travel on the Silk Road (Chapter 5, page 191)

_____

_____

_____

_____

_____

14. The British and Dutch Trading Empires (Chapter 10, page 345)

_____

_____

_____

_____

_____

_____

© Pearson Education, Inc., publishing as Pearson Prentice Hall. All rights reserved.

Concept Connector Study Guide

TRADE *(continued)*

15. United States Trade in the Twentieth Century (Chapter 19, page 663)

_____

_____

_____

_____

_____

_____

16. Fears About Foreign Trade Dominance (Chapter 19, page 663)

_____

_____

_____

_____

_____

_____

17. Modern Free Trade and Mercantilism in the 1600s and 1700s
(Chapter 19, page 663)

_____

_____

_____

_____

_____

_____

_____

© Pearson Education, Inc., publishing as Pearson Prentice Hall. All rights reserved.

Concept Connector Study Guide

TRADE *(continued)*

C. Sample Topics for Thematic Essays

Below are examples of thematic essay topics that might appear on a test. Prepare for the test by outlining an essay for each topic on a separate sheet of paper. Use the Concept Connector Handbooks at the end of your textbook, as well as chapter information, to outline your essays.

1. Discuss how the strong Roman military helped support trade during the *Pax Romana*, and how that trade then affected Roman civilization.

2. Describe the relationship between trade and the new European imperialism of the late 1800s.

3. Describe the British trade in cotton before the Industrial Revolution and how it was changed by the factory system.

4. Describe the importance of trade in Latin American nations before and after independence. How did trade have both positive and negative effects?

5. How was a favorable balance of trade an important part of Japan's growth after World War II?

6. Describe the development of the Common Market and European Union, and evaluate their impact on trade among member nations.

7. Describe the international treaties or organizations and the regional trade blocs that have been set up to promote trade. What are the goals of these treaties, organizations, and trade blocs?

8. What are the benefits of global trade? Why do some people oppose globalization?

© Pearson Education, Inc., publishing as Pearson Prentice Hall. All rights reserved.